Every fish that swims silent, every bird that flies freely
Every doe that steps softly
Every crisp leaf that falls, all the flowers that grow
On this colorful tapestry, somehow they know
That if man is allowed to destroy all we need
He will soon have to pay with his life
For his greed.

—Don McLean

The Sierra Club
survival
songbook

collected and edited by Jim Morse and Nancy Mathews
introduction by Pete Seeger
illustrated by Jos. A. Smith

in order of appearance:

Don McLean
Bill Steele
Joe McDonald
Malvina Reynolds
Tom Lehrer
Billy Edd Wheeler
Mike Kellin
Grant Rogers
Toni Brown
Janet Smith
Peter Seeger
Nancy Schimmel
Patrick Sky
Matt McGinn
Jimmy Collier
Suzanne Harris
Ric Masten
Peter LaFarge
Tom Paxton
Mayf Nutter
Dottie Gittelson
Mark Spoelstra
Ewan MacColl
Jean Ritchie
John Edmiston
Peter Hennessy
Ernie Marrs
Harold Martin
Rick Shaw
Dick Clark
John D. Loudermilk
John Nutting
Len H. Chandler, Jr.
Eric Andersen

Sierra Club   San Francisco ▪ New York

Designed and produced by Charles Curtis and printed in the
United States of America by Grafix.

The Sierra Club, founded in 1892 by John Muir, has devoted itself
to the study and protection of the nation's scenic and ecological
resources—mountains, wetlands, woodlands, wild shores and
rivers. All club publications are part of the nonprofit effort the
club carries on as a public trust. There are 34 chapters coast
to coast, in Hawaii and Alaska. Participation is invited in the
club's program to enjoy and preserve wilderness everywhere.
Address: 1050 Mills Tower, San Francisco, California 94104;
250 West 57th Street, New York, N.Y. 10019, or 235 Massachu-
setts Avenue N.E., Washington, D.C. 20002.

Halfnote

The 59 songs presented in this collection speak for themselves, as do their writers and composers. So do not expect to find any fancy footnotes or annotations as to why or how or when a particular number was put down. The important thing is *what* you have here. And what you have is a wide sampling of the best environmental songs in America today.

Please note that the first verse of every song appears not only with the music but is repeated again with the rest of the verses. This is for the guy or gal looking over the instrumentalist's shoulder. And for all those long-neglected types who want to sing along but can't read music. The music, incidentally, is for guitar. Pianists are asked to improvise.

—The Editors

Table of Contents

Introduction

Songs won't save our planet.
But then, neither will books or speeches.
How will it be saved?
By changing our course of action.
How will our present course be changed?
When our heads are turned around.
How do our heads get turned around?
By seeing more clearly: where we are going,
        where we have come from,
        where we are right now.
"Learn from the mistakes of others;
"You can't live long enough to make 'em all yourself."

Songs are sneaky things.
They can slip across borders,
Proliferate in prisons,
Penetrate hard shells.
(Keep in mind: what is an irresistible
 song to one person
 is a pain in the ear to another.)

(Keep in mind also: it's hard to perceive
 the real flavor of a song
 from the printed page.)

In this volume are calypso-type melodies,
 blues, laments, satires,
 ballads, glad songs, mad songs.
They have been made up by songwriters
 using the only tools they have
 to try and turn people's heads
 around.
What they would like you to do now (and
 I think I can speak for the rest,
 since I'm one of 'em) is that you
Commit some of your favorites to memory.
And take them with you on your travels.
And pass them on to others.

A song on a shelf is in a state of
Suspended animation.
You must bring them to life.
Such is their magic, they can bring
 fuller life to you.
And all of us together
May be able to help

Survival.

      Take it easy but take it,

      Pete Seeger

      April 1971
      Beacon, N.Y.

tapestry

Written by Don McLean

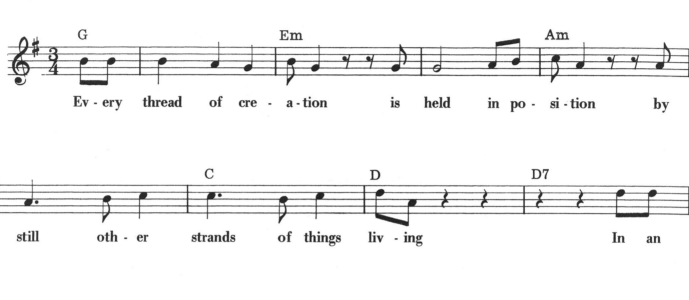

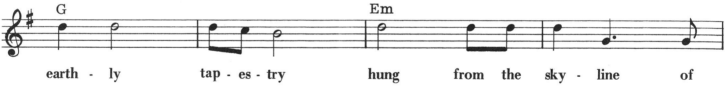

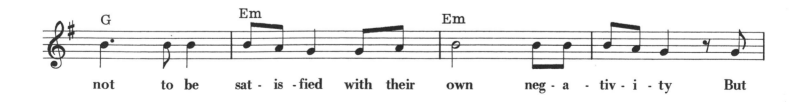

1. Every thread of creation is held in position
   By still other strands of things living
   In an earthly tapestry hung from the skyline of smoldering cities
   So gray and so vulgar as not to be satisfied with their own negativity
   But needing to touch all the living as well.

2. Every breeze that blows kindly is one crystal breath
   We exhale on the blue diamond heaven
   As gentle to touch as the hands of the healer
   As soft as farewells whispered over the coffin
   We're poisoned with venom with each breath we take
   From the brown sulphur chimney
   And the black highway snake.

3. Every dawn that breaks golden is held in suspension
   Like the yolk of the egg in albumen
   Where the birth and the death of unseen generations
   Are interdependent in vast orchestration
   And painted in colors of tapestry thread
   When the dying are born and the living are dead.

4. Every pulse of your heartbeat is one liquid moment
   That flows through the veins of your being
   Like a river of life flowing on since creation
   Approaching the sea with each new generation
   You're now just a stagnant and rancid disgrace
   That is rapidly drowning the whole human race.

5. Every fish that swims silent, every bird that flies freely
   Every doe that steps softly
   Every crisp leaf that falls, all the flowers that grow
   On this colorful tapestry, somehow they know
   That if man is allowed to destroy all we need
   He will soon have to pay with his life
   For his greed.

11

garbage

Words and music by Bill Steele

Mis - ter Thomp-son calls the wai-ter, or - ders steak and baked po - ta - to But he leaves the bone and gris - tle and he nev - er eats the skins; Then the bus boy comes and takes it, with a cough con - tam - i - nates it As he puts it in a can with cof - fee grounds and sar - dine tins; Then the truck comes by on Fri - day and carts it all a - way; And a thou-sand trucks just like it are con - verg - ing on the bay. Gar - bage! Gar-bage! We're fill -ing up the sea with gar-bage. Gar-bage! Gar-bage! What will we do when there's no place left to put all the gar-bage? Mis - ter noth-ing left to read, and there's noth-ing left to be but gar - bage. noth-ing left to hear, and there's

(Repeat measure as needed)

etc.

1. Mister Thompson calls the waiter, orders steak and baked potato
   But he leaves the bone and gristle and he never eats the skins;
   Then the bus boy comes and takes it, with a cough contaminates it
   As he puts it in a can with coffee grounds and sardine tins;
   Then the truck comes by on Friday and carts it all away;
   And a thousand trucks just like it are converging on the bay.
   Garbage! Garbage! We're filling up the sea with garbage.
   Garbage! Garbage!
   What will we do when there's no place left to put all the garbage?

2. Mister Thompson starts his Cadillac and winds it up
        the freeway track
   Leaving friends and neighbors in a hydrocarbon haze
   He's joined by lots of smaller cars all sending gasses to the stars
   There to form a seething cloud that hangs for thirty days
   While the sun licks down upon it with its ultraviolet tongues
   'Til it turns to smog and settles down and ends up in our lungs.
   Garbage! Garbage! We're filling up the sky with garbage.
   Garbage! Garbage!
   What will we do when there's nothing left to breathe but garbage?

3. Getting home and taking off his shoes he settles down
        with evening news
   While the kids do homework with the TV in one ear
   While Superman for thousandth time sells talking dolls
        and conquers crime
   They dutifully learn the date of birth of Paul Revere
   In the paper there's a piece about the mayor's middle name
   And he gets it done in time to watch the All-Star Bingo Game
   Garbage! Garbage! We're filling up our minds with garbage!
   Garbage! Garbage!
   What will we do when there's nothing left to read
        and there's nothing left to hear and there's nothing left to need
        and there's nothing left to wear and there's nothing left
           to talk about
        and nothing left to walk upon and nothing left to care about
        and nothing left to ponder on and nothing left to touch
        and there's nothing left to see and there's nothing left to do
        and there's nothing left to be — but garbage?

the hand of man

By Joe McDonald

Well it's man-y an hour I've spent think-in' of my fate

Doomed, it seemed, to live in a world of death and hate. I've

thought a-bout the love and the good that there should be How

hate can blind a man, how peo-ple are not free.

Chorus:

Take my

hand, come walk with me Bro-thers and sis-ters we

all shall be And from the spark set in the dark, From the hand of___

man Bro-ther-hood and love shall spread through-out our land.

1. Well it's many an hour I've spent thinkin' of my fate
   Doomed, it seemed, to live in a world of death and hate
   I've thought about the love and the good that there should be
   How hate can blind a man, how people are not free.

   Chorus:

   Take my hand, come walk with me
   Brothers and sisters we all shall be
   And from the spark set in the dark,
   From the hand of man
   Brotherhood and love shall spread throughout our land.

2. I gazed into the sky and saw the rains come down
   The precious blood of man flowed freely on the ground
   All hope of understanding drowned in one giant wave
   All years of effort wasted there was nothing left to save.

3. From the icy wind of winter to the cold and frozen plain
   In the darkness of the night a candle glows again
   And from a spark set in the dark from the hand of man
   Brotherhood and love spread throughout our land.

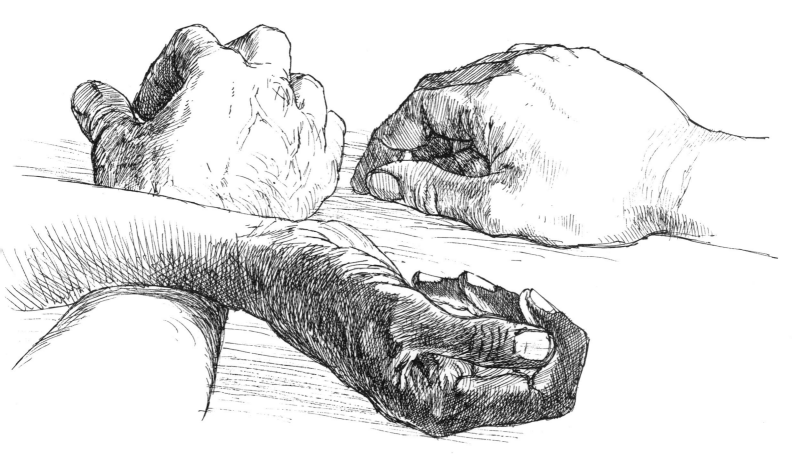

the faucets are dripping

Words and music by Malvina Reynolds

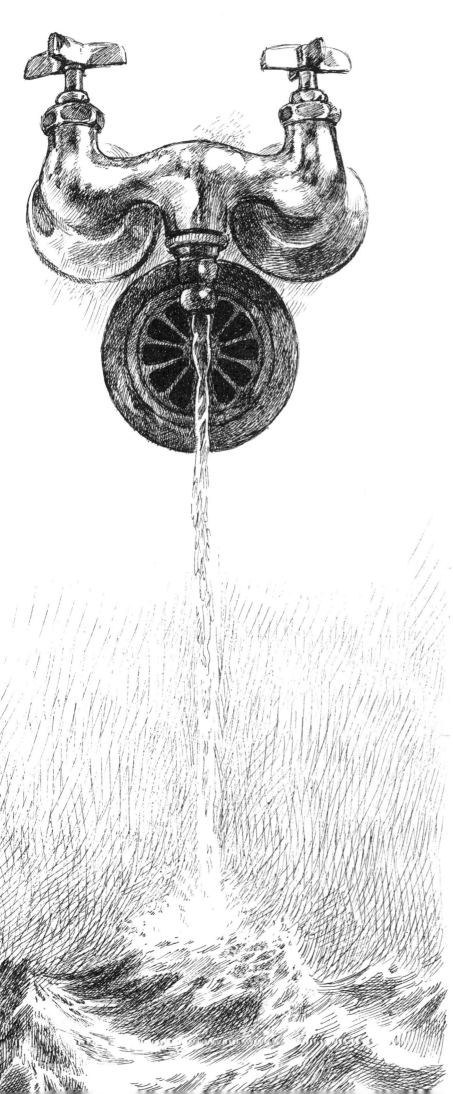

Chorus:
The faucets are dripping in old New York City,
The faucets are dripping, and oh, what a pity,
The reservoir's drying,
Because it's supplying
The faucets that drip in New York.

1. You can't ask the landlord to put in a
      washer,
   He'd rather you'd move than to put in
      a washer,
   The faucets are dripping, they sound in
      my ears,
   The tap in the bathroom's been running
      for years.

2. There's a wild streak of green in the
      sink in the kitchen,
   It comes from the rill trickling out of
      the plumbing,
   The streams from the mountains, the
      pools from the lea,
   All run from my faucet and down to the
      sea.

3. You can't ask the landlord to put in a
      washer,
   You can't ask the landlord to mend the
      old stairs,
   He takes in the rents and he lives in
      Miami
   Where faucets don't drip and there's
      sun everywheres.

pollution

By Tom Lehrer

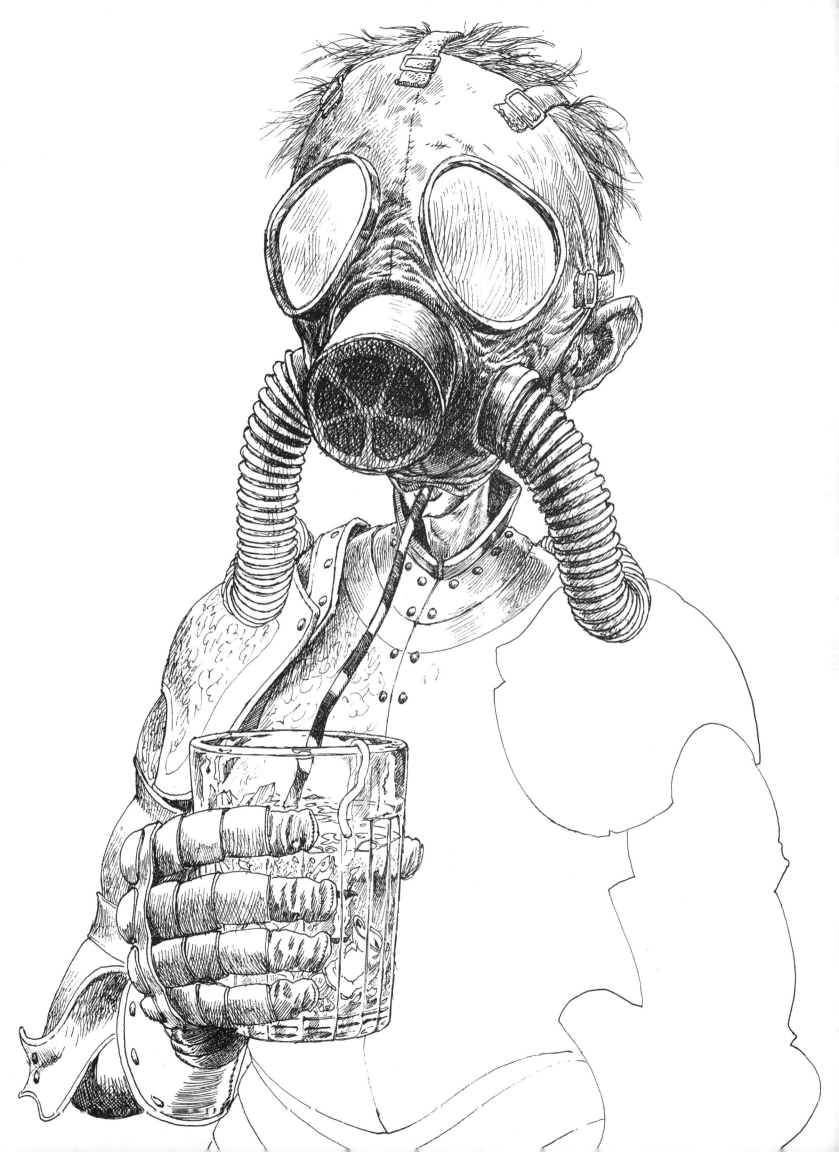

lu - tion,___ You can use the lat - est tooth - paste, And

then rinse___ your mouth with___ in - dus - tri - al waste.

3. Just go out___ for a breath of air,___ And you'll be read - y for

Med - i - care,___ The cit - y streets___ are real - ly

quite a thrill, ___ If the hoods don't get you, the mon -

ox - ide will.___ Pol - lu - tion,___ Pol - lu - tion,___ wear a

gas mask and a veil,_____ Then you___ can breathe long___ as

you don't___ in - hale. slaugh - ter,___

They're drink - ing___ the wa - ter___ and

breath - ing (cough..........) the air._____

1. If you visit American city,
   You will find it very pretty.
   Just two things of which you must beware:
   Don't drink the water and don't breathe the air.
   Pollution, Pollution,
   They got smog and sewage and mud,
   Turn on your tap and get hot and cold running crud.

2. See the halibuts and the sturgeons
   Being wiped out by detergeons.
   Fish gotta swim and birds gotta fly,
   But they don't last long if they try.
   Pollution, Pollution,
   You can use the latest toothpaste,
   And then rinse your mouth with industrial waste.

3. Just go out for a breath of air,
   And you'll be ready for Medicare,
   The city streets are really quite a thrill,
   If the hoods don't get you, the monoxide will.
   Pollution, Pollution,
   Wear a gas mask and a veil,
   Then you can breathe long as you don't inhale.

4. Lots of things there that you can drink,
   But stay away from the kitchen sink,
  *Throw out your breakfast garbage, and I've got a hunch,
   That the folks downstream will drink it for lunch.
   So go to the city, see the crazy people there,
   Like lambs to the slaughter,
   They're drinking the water and breathing *(cough)* the air.

*Alternate lyrics may be used here to fit the local situation, e.g.,

for New York: The breakfast garbage they throw out in Troy
                     They drink at lunch in Perth Amboy.

for San Francisco: The breakfast garbage that you throw into the Bay
                     They drink at lunch in San Jose.

coming of the roads

Words and music by Billy Edd Wheeler

Moderato

1. Oh now that our moun - tain is grow - ing with peo - ple hun - gry for wealth, How come it's you that's a - go - ing, and I'm left a - lone by my - self? We used to hunt the cool cav - erns deep in our for - est of green. Then came the road and the tav - erns, and you found a new love it seems. Oh once I had you and the wild - wood; Now it's just dus - ty roads, And I can't help from blam - ing your go - ing on the com - ing, The Com - ing Of The Roads.

1. Oh now that our mountain is growing
   With people hungry for wealth,
   How come it's you that's a-going,
   And I'm left alone by myself?
   We used to hunt the cool caverns
   Deep in our forest of green.
   Then came the road and the taverns,
   And you found a new love it seems.
   Oh once I had you and the wildwood;
   Now it's just dusty roads,
   And I can't help from blaming your going
   On the coming, the coming of the roads.

2. Oh look how they've cut all to pieces
   Our ancient poplar and oak.
   And the hillsides are stained with the greases
   That burned up the heavens with smoke.
   You used to curse the bold crewmen
   Who stripped our earth of its ore.
   But you've changed, and you've gone over to them
   And you've learned to love what you hated before.
   Oh once I thanked God for my treasure,
   Now it, like rust, corrodes,
   And I can't help from blaming your going
   On the coming, the coming of the roads.

don't dump it in the river!

Words and music by Mike Kellin

She told me that she loved me _____ then she tore my

soul in twain. _____ As I stood on the shore with my bleed - ing

heart she sang this sad re - frain _____ Don't

dump it in the riv - er! _____ Don't dump it

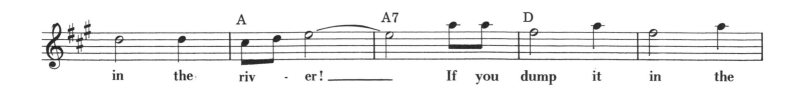

in the riv - er! _____ If you dump it in the

riv - er poor boy, you'll on - ly make it worse! _____

1. She told me that she loved me then she tore my soul in twain
   As I stood on the shore with my bleeding heart she sang this sad refrain:

   Chorus:
   Don't dump it in the river! Don't dump it in the river!
   If you dump it in the river, poor boy, you'll only make it worse!

2. I was so doggone heartsick that I sailed off to sea
   Then I was so doggone seasick that the captain said to me

3. I swam ashore in Nyack and crawled into my bed
   And upstream there was Greta, picketing Con Ed

4. Next day came a letter from Nixon, said, "Draftee, make us proud"
   I took his greetings down to the shore, and the fishes cried out loud

5. I wrote farewell to Greta, said, "Greta, I'm goin' away"
   She answered, "If you must, you must, just wait for garbage day"

6. So go an' have your singing, an' go an' sail your sloop
   And as for all the garbage you leave, I'll leave you with this poop

cannonsville dam

By Grant Rogers

Friends just lend an ear and lis-ten to a sto-ry sad, but true, While our fami-lies, friends and neigh-bors search for dis-tant lands so new._____ We've been told that we must leave our homes,_ From this val-ley we love so dear, To make room for the dam they're build-ing here._____ To make room for the dam they're build-ing here._____ If you ev-er met a lit-tle child, from you he is-n't sure, If he asked you for some

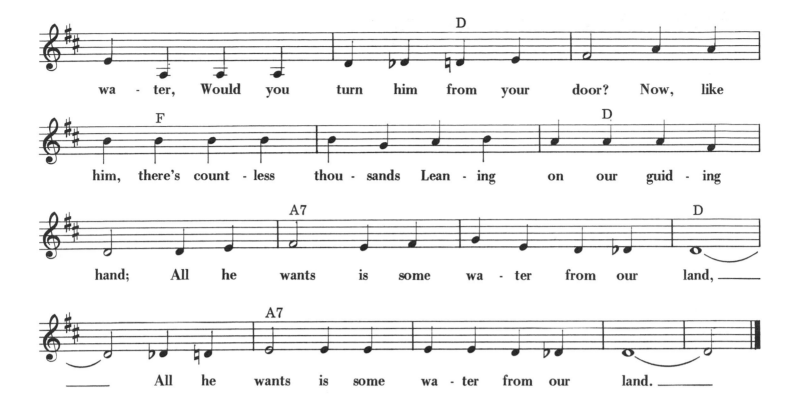

wa - ter, Would you turn him from your door? Now, like
him, there's count - less thou - sands Lean - ing on our guid - ing
hand; All he wants is some wa - ter from our land, _____
_____ All he wants is some wa - ter from our land. _____

1. Friends just lend an ear and listen
   To a story sad, but true,
   While our families, friends and neighbors
   Search for distant lands so new.
   We've been told that we must leave our homes,
   From this valley we love so dear,
   To make room for the dam they're building here,
   To make room for the dam they're building here.

   If you ever met a little child,
   From you he isn't sure.
   If he asked you for some water,
   Would you turn him from your door?
   Now, like him, there's countless thousands
   Leaning on our guiding hand;
   All he wants is some water from our land,
   All he wants is some water from our land.

2. When the flood comes to the valley,
   Spanning miles from shore to shore,
   Then we realize, as humans,
   We could have done but little more.
   There'll be many a heart that's broken
   Among the young as well as old.
   For they'll never see the old homes anymore,
   No they'll never see the old homes anymore.

   You have read of good old Moses,
   With the rod did smite the rock;
   Then came water for the multitude,
   Water for the flock.
   Now the same has come to us today
   Like many years ago.
   We wouldn't turn our backs upon our friends;
   We wouldn't tell them 'no'.
   We wouldn't turn our backs upon our friends;
   We wouldn't tell them 'no'.

children's house

By Toni Brown

As I walk the still green hills
waiting for the winter rains
Looking out at what's before me
and all that still remains.

I think about past generations
as the gulls fly seaward overhead
Indians who danced here have been forgotten
and who will dance here when I'm dead.

This is our children's house
and they wait outside the door
They're listening to our voices
and learning what we think we're here for.

Do we know and can we tell them
as our own fathers live out their lie
As we grow sick and tired from watching
how they've let the earth slip by.

This is no mansion now
it's dust is filling up the sky
We must repair some how
or be haunted by our children's cry.

Do we know and can we tell them
what it means to be a man
For we are living in our children's house
and they will follow only if they can.

johnny's lullabye

Words and music by Janet Smith

Chorus:

Go to sleep, sweet John - ny, my ba - by; _____ Lul - la -
bye till __ morn - ing, my dar - ling lit - tle one. When you
wake, the world will be wait - ing? go to sleep, my
ba - by, my son. sleep, my ba - by, my son;
When you wake, the world will be wait - ing.
Will you say the same thing to your son?

Verse:

1. Oh, the sky was a lit - tle bit blu - er years a - go, when
I was quite young; but the air is still fresh in the
moun - tains, will you say the same thing to your son?

Chorus:

Go to sleep, sweet Johnny, my baby;
Lullabye till morning, my darling little one.
When you wake, the world will be waiting;
Go to sleep, my baby, my son.

1. Oh, the sky was a little bit bluer
   Years ago, when I was quite young,
   But the air is still fresh in the mountains,
   Will you say the same thing to your son?

2. Oh the forests that grew on the hillside
   Years ago when I was quite young
   Now are fewer but man has crossed over
   Will you say the same thing to your son?

3. Oh the river that flowed through our valley
   Years ago when I was quite young
   No one fishes or swims any more there
   Will you say the same thing to your son?

we'll all be a-doubling

Words and music by Pete Seeger

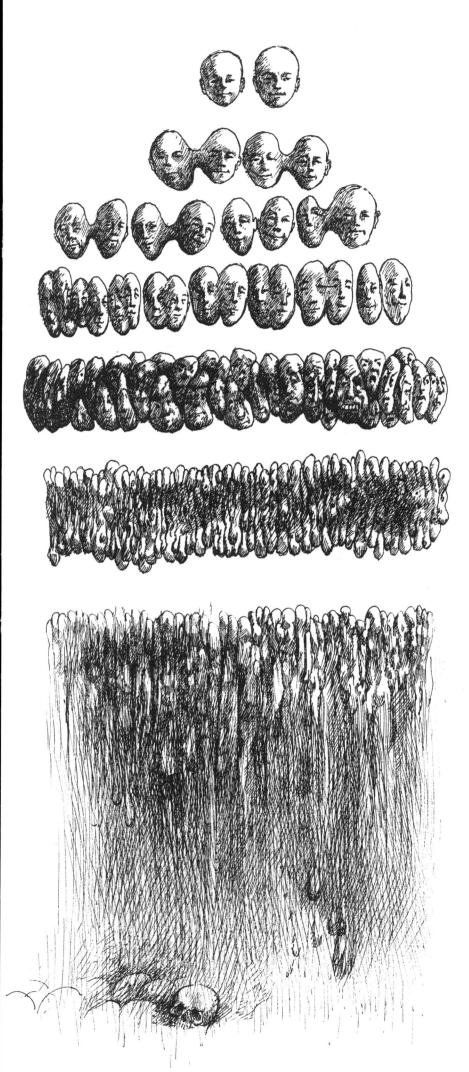

Chorus:

We'll all be a-doubling, a-doubling, a-doubling,
We'll all be a-doubling in thirty-two years.
We'll all be a-doubling, a-doubling, a-doubling,
We'll all be a-doubling in thirty-two years.

1. Two times two is four!
   Two times four is eight!
   Two times eight is sixteen,
   And the hour is getting late!

2. Two times sixteen is thirty-two
   Twice that is sixty-four
   Next comes a hundred twenty-eight
   And do you want to hear more?

3. Next comes two hundred fifty-six
   Twice that is five hundred and twelve
   Next, one thousand twenty-four
   Just figure it out yourself.

4. Next two thousand forty-eight
   Then four thousand ninety-six
   Eight thousand, one hundred ninety-two
   Some parent is a-looking sick.

5. Every eight generations
   Multiply a thousand times
   Sixteen makes it a million
   Some people don't like this rhyme.

6. Give it another three hundred years
   Your children number a billion.
   Keep doubling another millenium
   You can have another quadrillion.

7. For two thousand years we been praying
   O Lord, deliver me please
   The Lord helps them that help themselves
   We better get off our knees.

8. Either people are going to have to get smaller
   Or the world's going to have to get bigger
   Or there's a couple other possibilities
   I'll leave it to you to figger.

don't

By Nancy Schimmel

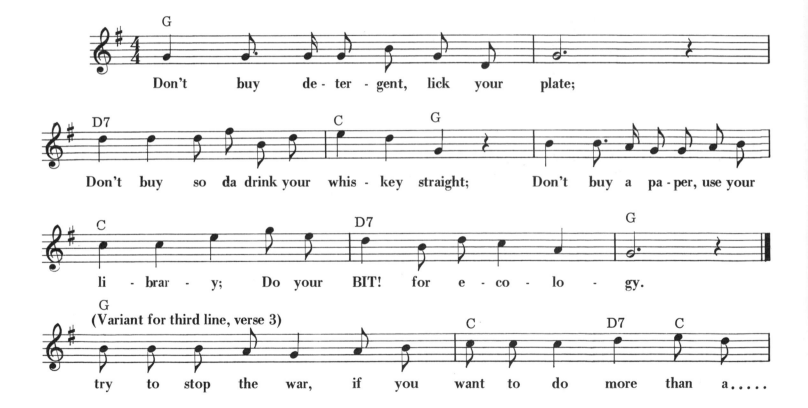

1. Don't buy detergent, lick your plate;
   Don't buy soda, drink your whiskey straight;
   Don't buy a paper, use your library;
   Do your BIT! for ecology.

2. Don't use a tissue, sniff instead;
   Don't use a napkin, use a piece of bread;
   Don't flush the toilet every time you pee;
   Do your BIT! for ecology.

3. Now think about defoliant spray.
   We are dropping umpty tons a day.
   Try to stop the war, if you want to do more
   Than a BIT! for ecology.

the emperor's nightingale

Words and music by Malvina Reynolds

swing it *

2. Some big - time pro - mot - ers, they gath - ered to - geth - er, They said, "There's a for - tune in that lit - tle soul. Fif - ti - eth and Broad - way is our pri - vate road - way if we can get Night - in - gale un - der con - trol." Then one of the crew said, "That bird is a pho - ny, He's lit - tle and bon - y, His feath - ers are gray. We'll fix up a sing - er who'll be a real swing - er, e - lec - tron - ic mar - vel who'll war - ble all day. 3. An - 4. The King thanked them kind - ly, the court was en - chant - ed, they were in - stant - ly grant - ed a mil - lion or more. It was ea - sy as noth - ing, you just pressed the but - ton and mus - ic came roll - ing on ev - er - y floor. 5. But with

38   * This can also be done in the original key of C

1. The Emperor's nightingale sang in the forest,
   And the Emperor listened to hear his sweet song.
   The bird was his treasure and sang for his pleasure,
   And the Emperor listened the whole evening long.
   And the nightingale sang as his small heart dictated.
   The song he created was gentle and true,
   And all those who heard him were eased of their burden,
   The King and the court and the woodcutter, too.

2. Some big-time promoters, they gathered together,
   They said, "There's a fortune in that little soul.
   Fiftieth and Broadway is our private roadway
   If we can get Nightingale under control."
   Then one of the crew said, "That bird is a phony,
   He's little and bony, his feathers are gray.
   We'll fix up a singer who'll be a real swinger,
   Electronic marvel who'll warble all day."

3. Another one said, "That's a dandy promotion,
   A handier notion I seldom have heard!
   We'll make one real classy, with platinum chassis.
   Oh brother won't we give His Kingship the bird!"
   So they fixed up a chirp that was really a wonder,
   With woofers and tweeters, transistors and those,
   And the whole bit was rolled in a body all golden,
   With emerald eyes that could open and close.

4. The King thanked them kindly, the court was enchanted,
   They were instantly granted a million or more.
   It was easy as nothing, you just pressed the button
   And music came rolling on every floor.

5. But with kings and with courts you can never be certain.
   They tired of the chirp's high fidelity song.
   With no singer near him and no bird to cheer him,
   The Emperor's evenings were weary and long.
   For the Emperor's nightingale, he had departed.
   He could not be found tho' they looked ev'rywhere,
   For the dear little fella was singing cappella
   On the very last tree left in Washington Square.

manhattan, manhattan

By Patrick Sky

Moderately

Chorus:

Man - hat-tan, Man - hat-tan, you're a hid - e - ous sight, It's dark in the day - time, it's

light - er at night; I won't ride the E Train be - cause it's a sin And I

hope I won't see a god - dam cab - bie a - gain.   gain.

To Verses   *Fine*

Verse:

1. Well old New York Cit - y's a won - der - ful place, That is if you

like to get dirt on your face; The air is so thick it - 'll

D.C. al Fine

cause you to choke, If you want to stay heal - thy breathe New Jer - sey smoke.

Chorus:
Manhattan, Manhattan, you're a hideous sight,
It's dark in the day time, it's lighter at night;
I won't ride the E Train because it's a sin
And I hope I won't see a goddam cabbie again.

1. Well old New York City's a wonderful place,
   That is if you like to get dirt on your face;
   The air is so thick it'll cause you to choke,
   If you want to stay healthy breathe New Jersey smoke.

2. Con Edison, Con Edison, you beautiful thing
   I dream of you each night from my heart-lung machine
   I dream as the undertakers gather my dust
   There's a stone round their necks that's inscribed "Dig we must".

3. East River, East River, your water's so pure
   I'll take me a potful to the City Hall door
   I'll scream in defiance right there in the yard
   And as a protesting gesture I'll boil my draft card.

old devil time

By Peter Seeger

1. Old Devil Time, I'm goin' to fool you now!
   Old Devil Time, you'd like to bring me down!
   When I'm feeling low, my lovers gather 'round
   And help me rise to fight you one more time!

2. Old Devil Fear, you with your icy hands,
   Old Devil Fear, you'd like to freeze me cold!
   But when I'm afraid my lovers gather 'round
   And help me rise to fight you one more time!

3. Old Devil Pain, you often pinned me down,
   You thought I'd cry, and beg you for the end.
   But at that very time my lovers gather 'round
   And help me rise to fight you one more time!

4. Old Devil Hate, I knew you long ago,
   Then I found out the poison in your breath.
   Now when we hear your lies my lovers gather 'round
   And help me rise to fight you one more time!

5. No storm or fire can ever beat us down,
   No wind that blows but carries us further on.
   And you who fear, o lovers, gather 'round
   And we can rise, and sing it one more time!

little boxes

Words and music by Malvina Reynolds

1. Little boxes on the hillside,
   Little boxes made of ticky tacky,
   Little boxes on the hillside,
   Little boxes all the same.
   There's a green one and a pink one
   And a blue one and a yellow one
   And they're all made out of ticky tacky
   And they all look just the same.

2. And the people in the houses
   All went to the university,
   Where they were put in boxes
   And they came out all the same,
   And there's doctors and lawyers,
   And business executives,
   And they're all made out of ticky tacky
   And they all look just the same.

3. And they all play on the golf course
   And drink their martinis dry,
   And they all have pretty children
   And the children go to school,
   And the children go to summer camp
   And then to the university,
   Where they are put in boxes
   And they come out all the same

4. And the boys go into business
   And marry and raise a family
   In boxes made of ticky tacky
   And they all look just the same.
   There's a green one and a pink one,
   And a blue one and a yellow one,
   And they're all made out of ticky tacky
   And they all look just the same.

the pill

By Matt McGinn

Chorus:
The pill, ___ the pill, ___ I'm pi - ning for the pill ___ I'll nev - er have an - y more be - cause they're going to bless the pill.

Verse:
I wed when I was sev - en - teen, I had nae man - y brains, ___ says I the ver - y thing to do is fill the hoose wi' weans, ___ But when I had the room - ful I went to see the priest, ___ to tell him my man Wil - lie was be - hav - ing like a beast. ___

D. C. al Fine

Chorus:

The pill, the pill, I'm pining for the pill.
I'll never have any more because they're going to bless the pill.

1. I wed when I was seventeen, I had nae many brains,
   Says I the very thing to do is fill the hoose wi' weans,
   But when I had the roomful I went to see the priest,
   To tell him my man Willie was behaving like a beast.

2. He gave me such a terrible row my eyes were filled wi' tears,
   "How long have you been wed?" says he; says I, "This seven years."
   Says he, "You'd better give over all your evil sinful tricks,
   You've been married seven years and you've only got the six."

3. Now I'm coming up for forty in my faith I've aye been true,
   The very last time I tallied them I counted twenty-two.
   But now I've lost the notion for we're running short o' names,
   Though Willie he would welcome more — he's fond o' having weans.

4. Now they're talking o' the pill they've filled my heart wi' hope,
   I'm sitting here and waiting on a signal frae the Pope,
   I went along to buy some at fifteen bob a tin,
   I hope we hae the Pope's O.K. before my man comes in.

let it be

Words and music by Malvina Reynolds

When you walk in the for-est, let it be. There's a flow-er in the wood, let it be. There's a flow-er in the wood, and it's in-no-cent and good, By the stone where it stands let it be. Let it be, let it be, It's so love-ly where it is, let it be. Tho you want it for your own, if you take it from its place, It will not be what it was when you loved it where it stood in the wood. Let it be, let it be. It's so love-ly where it is, let it be. It's a thought-ful child, in-no-cent and wild, By the stone, by the reed, Let it bloom, let it seed, Let it be.

1. When you walk in the forest, let it be.
   There's a flower in the wood, let it be.
   There's a flower in the wood, and it's innocent and good,
   By the stone where it stands let it be.

2. Let it be, let it be,
   It's so lovely where it is, let it be.
   Tho you want it for your own, if you take it from its place,
   It will not be what it was when you loved it where it stood in the wood.

3. Let it be, let it be.
   It's so lovely where it is, let it be.
   It's a thoughtful child, innocent and wild,
   By the stone, by the reed,
   Let it bloom, let it seed,
   Let it be.

lead poison on the wall

Words and music by Jimmy Collier

Chorus:
Lead poison on the wall,
Kills little guys and little dolls.
It kills 'em big and it kills 'em small,
While we stand by and watch them fall,
And the landlord does a-nothing to stop it all,
That death on the wall,
That death on the wall.

1. There's poison in the paint
   Enough to make a little child faint,
   Enough to blind his eye,
   Enough to make him die, from that

2. There's plaster falling from the ceiling
   Plaster falling and plaster peeling,
   Doesn't the landlord have any feeling?
   Someone's responsible for all that killing
   From the —

3. Urine samples and knockin' on doors
   Label of paint in all of the stores
   Rally and action and you cannot ignore
   There's still children dying,
   So we've got to do more on that—

here come the beautiful people

Words and music by Suzanne Harris

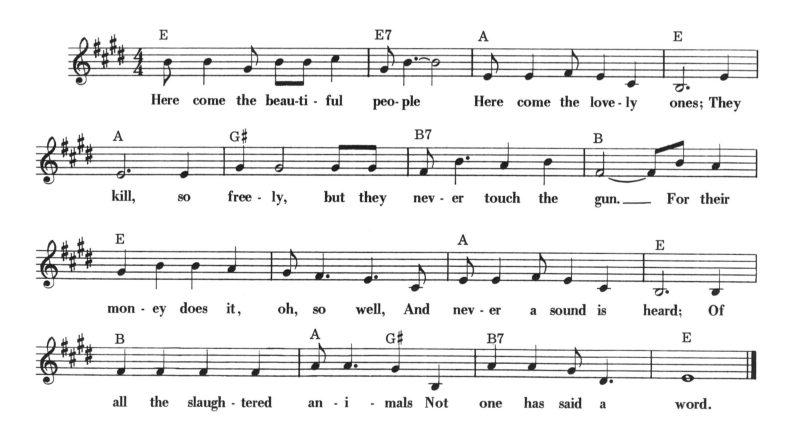

Here come the beau-ti-ful peo-ple Here come the love-ly ones; They kill, so free-ly, but they nev-er touch the gun.___ For their mon-ey does it, oh, so well, And nev-er a sound is heard; Of all the slaugh-tered an-i-mals Not one has said a word.

Chorus:

Here come the beautiful people,
Here come the lovely ones;
They kill, so freely,
But they never touch the gun.
For their money does it, oh, so well,
And never a sound is heard;
Of all the slaughtered animals
Not one has said a word.

1. On a street in Boston
   She wears a leopard skin;
   She won't say where she's going,
   And she won't say where she's been.
   But her picture's worth a thousand words
   With its spots so black and round,
   And through the jungles leopards drop
   Like flies upon the ground.

2. A million years before us
   He lived upon this earth,
   But all we care to learn
   Is how much his hide is worth.
   And so his ancient secrets
   We'll forever lose,
   As closets round the world are filled
   With alligator shoes.

3. For a famous movie star
   Ten tigers had to die,
   So in her striped maxi-coat
   She turned each and every eye.
   And when a reporter questioned her,
   This is what she said:
   'I didn't kill a thing, you know,
   They were already dead.'

4. Here come the beauty experts
   With oils and creams that flow;
   They've got a billion-dollar business
   So they'll never let you know
   All the cruel tortures
   Behind the bottles they fill:
   Ladies, you can stop all this,
   For looks don't have to kill.

5. Here come the fashion magazines
   With something new to wear,
   Proclaiming true beauty
   Only comes to those who dare.
   And I wonder if the editors
   Have dared to realise,
   With their every furred and feathered page
   Our precious wildlife dies.

6. Why don't men raise and breed these animals
   Like a farmer would?
   But the businessman answers simply:
   'There's no reason why we should.
   For as long as there is wildlife
   Standing free upon the land,
   There's a handsome profit to be made
   By an enterprising man.'

the song of the world's last whale

By Peter Seeger

I heard the song ———— of the world's last whale, ——— —— As I rocked in the moon-light ———— and reefed the sail. ———— It-'ll hap-pen to you al - so with-out fail, if it hap-pens to me ———— sang the world's last whale. ———

1. I heard the song
   Of the world's last whale,
   As I rocked in the moonlight
   And reefed the sail.
   It'll happen to you
   Also without fail,
   If it happens to me
   Sang the world's last whale.

2. It was down off Bermuda
   Early last spring,
   Near an underwater mountain
   Where the humpbacks sing.
   I lowered the microphone
   A quarter mile down,
   Switched on the recorder
   And let the tape spin round.

3. I didn't just hear grunting,
   I didn't just hear squeaks,
   I didn't just hear bellows,
   I didn't just hear shrieks.
   It was the musical singing
   And the passionate wail
   That came from the heart
   Of the world's last whale.

4. Down in the Antarctic
   The harpoons wait,
   But it's up on the land
   They decide my fate.
   In London Town
   They'll be telling the tale,
   If it's life or death
   For the world's last whale.

5. So here's a little test
   To see how you feel,
   Here's a little test
   For this Age Of The Automobile.
   If we can save
   Our singers in the sea,
   Perhaps there's a chance
   To save you and me.

6. I heard the song
   Of the world's last whale,
   As I rocked in the moonlight
   And reefed the sail.
   It'll happen to you
   Also without fail,
   If it happens to me
   Sang the world's last whale.

seventy miles

Music by Pete Seeger, words by Malvina Reynolds

Sev - en - ty miles of wind and spray, — Sev - en - ty

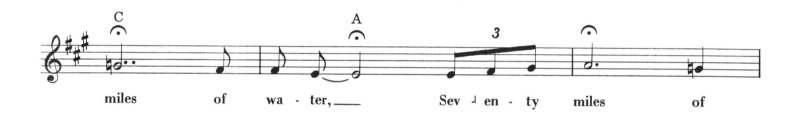

miles of wa - ter, —— Sev - en - ty miles of

o - pen Bay, —— It's a gar - bage dump.

What's that stink - y creek out there, Down be - hind the slums back - stair,

sludg - y pud - dle, sad and gray?_ Why man, that's San Fran - cis - co Bay! Sev - en - ty

Seventy miles of wind and spray,
Seventy miles of water,
Seventy miles of open Bay —
It's a garbage dump.

1. What's that stinky creek out there,
   Down behind the slum's back stair —
   Sludgy puddle, sad and gray?
   Why man, that's San Francisco Bay!

2. Big Solano and the Montecell',
   Ferry boats, I knew them well,
   Creak and groan in their muddy graves,
   Remembering old San Francisco Bay.

3. Joe Ortega and the Spanish crew
   Sailed across the ocean blue,
   Came into this mighty Bay,
   Stood on the decks and cried, "Ole!"

4. Fill it there, fill it here,
   Docks and tidelands disappear,
   Shaky houses on the quakey ground,
   The builder, he's Las Vegas bound.

5. "Dump the garbage in the Bay?"
   City fathers say, "Okay.
   When cries of anguish fill the air,
   We'll be off on the Riviere."

Seventy miles of wind and spray,
Seventy miles of water,
Seventy miles of open Bay —
It's a garbage dump.

goin' down the road feelin' bad

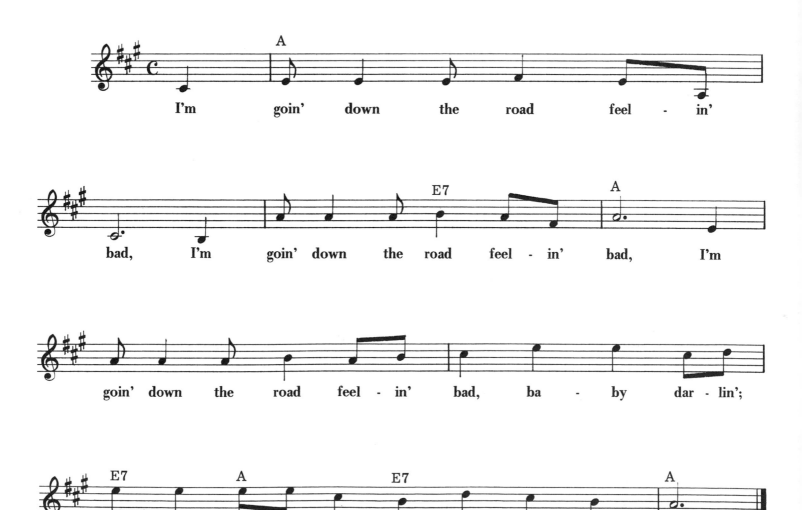

1. I'm goin' down the road feelin' bad,
   I'm goin' down the road feelin' bad,
   I'm goin' down the road feelin' bad, baby darlin';
   And I ain't goin' to be treated this way.

2. I'm down in the jail on my knees,
   I'm down in the jail on my knees,
   I'm down in the jail on my knees, baby darlin';
   And I ain't gonna be treated this way.

3. They fed me on cornbread and wine,
   They fed me on cornbread and wine,
   They fed me on cornbread and wine, baby darlin';
   And I ain't gonna be treated this way.

4. Takes a ten-dollar shoe to fit my foot,
   Takes a ten-dollar shoe to fit my foot,
   Takes a ten-dollar shoe to fit my foot, baby darlin';
   And I ain't gonna be treated this way.

5. Mississippi water tastes like turpentine,
   Mississippi water tastes like turpentine,
   Mississippi water tastes like turpentine, baby darlin';
   And I ain't gonna be treated this way.

6. I'm cold, lonely and I'm blue,
   I'm cold, lonely and I'm blue,
   I'm cold, lonely and I'm blue, baby darlin';
   And I ain't gonna be treated this way.

7. No one'll stir my gravy when I'm gone,
   No one'll stir my gravy when I'm gone,
   No one'll stir my gravy when I'm gone, baby darlin';
   And I ain't gonna be treated this way.

8. I'm goin' where the climate suits my clothes,
   I'm goin' where the climate suits my clothes,
   I'm goin' where the climate suits my clothes, baby darlin';
   And I ain't gonna be treated this way.

9. I'm goin' where the milk turns to wine,
   I'm goin' where the milk turns to wine,
   I'm goin' where the milk turns to wine, baby darlin';
   And I ain't gonna be treated this way.

10. I'm goin' where the chilly winds don't blow,
    I'm goin' where the chilly winds don't blow,
    I'm goin' where the chilly winds don't blow, baby darlin';
    And I ain't gonna be treated this way.

loneliness

By Ric Masten

1. Standin' by a highway
   Waitin' for a ride
   A bitter wind is blowin'
   It keeps you cold inside
   A line of cars is passin'
   No one seems to care
   You look down at your body
   To be sure you are there.

   Chorus:
   And this is loneliness,
   The kind that I have known
   If you've had times like this, my friend,
   You're not alone.

2. Sittin' in a hotel
   Starin' at the walls
   Cracks across the ceiling
   Silence in the halls
   You open up the window
   And turn the TV on
   Then you go down to the lobby
   But everybody's gone.

3. So you leave the empty cities
   And go down to the shore
   You're achin' to discover
   What you're lookin' for
   The beaches are deserted
   In the morning time
   A solitary figure
   You walk the water line.

4. You come upon a tidepool
   You stand there peerin' in
   And when you touch the water
   The circles do begin
   You look to where a seabird
   Lies crumpled on the sand
   Then you take a single pebble
   And hold it in your hand.

5. You come back up the beaches
   At the end of day
   And see how all your footprints
   Have been washed away
   Nothin' is forever
   We are born to die
   So may I say I love you
   Before I say good-bye - -
   I must say I love you - -
   And now I'll say good-bye.

orphans of wealth

Written by Don McLean

sea - sons re - volve ___ 'mid their sounds of star - va - tion ___ when the

tides ___ rise they cov - er the floor ___ They

And the rain falls ___ and blows through their win-dow and the snow falls ___

___ in white drifts that fold and the tides rise _____ with

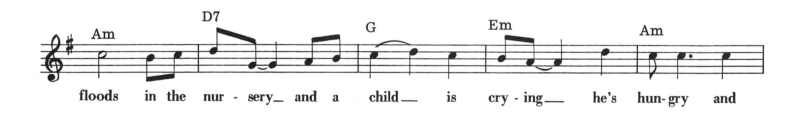

floods in the nur - sery ___ and a child ___ is cry - ing ___ he's hun-gry and

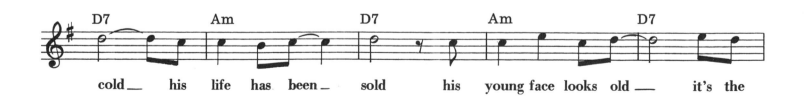

cold ___ his life has been ___ sold his young face looks old ___ it's the

face of A - mer - i - ca _____ dy - ing!

1. There is no time to discuss or debate
   What is right what is wrong for our people.
   Time has run out for all those who wait
   With bent limbs and minds that are feeble.

   Chorus:

   And the rain falls and blows through their window
   And the snow falls and blows through their door
   And the seasons revolve 'mid their sounds of starvation
   When the tides rise they cover the floor.

2. They come from the north and they come from the south
   And they come from the hills and the valleys
   And they're migrants and farmers and miners and humans
   Our census neglected to tally.

3. And they're African, Mexican, Caucasian, Indian
   Hungry and hopeless Americans
   The orphans of wealth and of adequate health
   Disowned by this nation they live in
   And with weather worn hands on bread lines they stand
   Yet but one more degradation.
   And they're treated like tramps while we sell them food stamps
   This thriving and prosperous nation.

4. And with roaches and rickets and rats in the thickets
   Infested, diseased and decaying,
   With rags and no shoes and skin sores that ooze
   By the poisonous pools they are playing
   In shacks of two rooms that are rotting wood tombs
   With corpses breathing inside them.
   And we pity their plight as they call in the night
   And we do all that we can do to hide them.

   Coda:

   And the rain falls and blows through their window
   And the snow falls in white drifts that fold
   And the tides rise with floods in the nursery
   And a child is crying
   He's hungry and cold
   His life has been sold
   His young face looks old
   It's the face of America dying!

coyote, my little brother

By Peter LaFarge

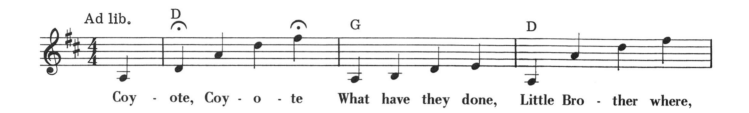

Coy - ote, Coy - o - te   What have they done,   Little Bro - ther where,

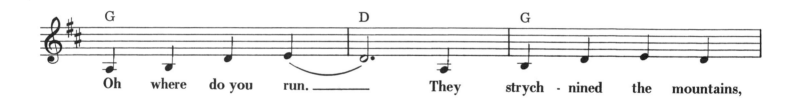

Oh   where   do you   run. _____   They   strych - nined   the   mountains,

They strychnined the   plains, _____   My little brother coyote   Won't come back.

Coyote, Coyote
What have they done,
Little Brother where,
Oh where do you run.

They strychnined the mountains,
They strychnined the plains,
My little brother the coyote
Won't come back again.

When you hear him singing,
The few that are left,
He is warning the human race,
Of his death.......

Don't poison the mesas,
Don't poison the skies,
Or you won't be back,
Little Brother goodbye.......

There will be no one to listen,
And no one to sing,
And never and never,
Will there be spring.

Coyote, Coyote,
What have they done,
Little Brother where,
Where do you run.......

my rainbow race

By Peter Seeger

1. One blue sky above us,
   One ocean, lapping all our shores,
   One earth so green and round,
   Who could ask for more?

2. And because I love you
   I'll give it one more try
   To show my rainbow race
   It's too soon to die.

3. Some folks want to be like an ostrich:
   Bury their heads in the sand
   Some hope for plastic dreams
   To unclench all those greedy hands.

4. Some want to take the easy way:
   Poison, bombs! They think we need 'em.
   Don't they know you can't kill all the unbelievers.
   There's no shortcut to freedom.

   (Repeat)

   One blue sky above us,
   One ocean, lapping all our shores,
   One earth so green and round,
   Who could ask for more?

   And because I love you
   I'll give it one more try
   To show my rainbow race
   It's too soon to die.

5. Go tell, go tell all the little children!
   Go tell mothers and fathers, too:
   Now's our last chance to learn to share
   What's been given to me and you.

   (Repeat)

   One blue sky above us,
   One ocean, lapping all our shores,
   One earth so green and round,
   Who could ask for more?

we will all go together when we go

By Tom Lehrer

When you attend a funeral,
It is sad to think that sooner o' later
Those you love will do the same for you.
And you may have thought it tragic,
Not to mention other adjectives,
To think of all the weeping they will do
(but don't you worry).
No more ashes, no more sackcloth,
And an armband made of black cloth
Will someday never more adorn a sleeve.
For if the bomb that drops on you
Gets your friends and neighbors too,
There'll be nobody left behind to grieve.

Chorus:

1. And We Will All Go Together When We Go,
   What a comforting fact that is to know.
   Universal bereavement,
   An inspiring achievement,
   Yes, we all will go together when we go.
   We Will All Go Together When We Go.
   All suffused with an incandescent glow.
   No one will have the endurance to collect on his insurance,
   Lloyd's of London will be loaded when they go.
   We will all fry together when we fry.
   We'll be french fried potatoes bye and bye.
   There will be no more misery when the world is our rotisserie,
   Yes, we all will fry together when we fry.
   Down by the old maelstrom,
   There'll be a storm before the calm.

2. And we will all bake together when we bake,
   There'll be nobody present at the wake.
   With complete participation,
   In that grand incineration,
   Nearly three billion hunks of well-done steak.
   We will all char together when we char.
   And let there be no moaning of the bar.
   Just sing out a Te Deum when you see that I.C.B.M.,
   And the party will be come-as-you-are.
   We will all burn together when we burn.
   There'll be no need to stand and wait your turn.
   When it's time for the fallout and Saint Peter calls us all out,
   We'll just drop our agendas and adjourn.
   You will all go directly to your respective Valhallas.
   Go directly, do not pass go, do not collect two hundred dolla's.
   And We Will All Go Together When We Go,
   Ev'ry Hottentot and ev'ry Eskimo.
   When the air becomes uranious,
   We will all go simultaneous,
   Yes, we all will go together when we all go together,
   Yes, we all will go together when we go.

there'll come a time

Words and music by Malvina Reynolds

There'll come a time the smog will be so thick,

We'll all have to walk with a long white walk - ing stick,

But we won't walk an - y - how, We'll go by air,

And the hel - i - cop - ters will be so thick we won't get an - y - where.

Chorus: There'll come a time, be - lieve me, son, And

when that day is here, I will be gone.

Last time: And by that time I'll be play - ing an un - am - pli - fied

harp on an eigh - teenth cen - tu - ry cloud.

1. There'll come a time the smog will be so thick
   We'll all have to walk with a long white walking stick,
   But we won't walk anyhow, we'll go by air,
   And the helicopters will be so thick we won't get anywhere.

   Chorus:

   There'll come a time,
   Believe me, son,
   And when that day is here, I will be gone.

2. Such adulteration will have hit the food,
   You'll throw way the contents and eat the carton if you want anything good.
   And women will live on synthetic meals,
   And they'll all be slender as synthetic eels.

3. There'll come a time the kids will be so smart,
   They'll be able to recite their own psychoanalysis by heart,
   And they'll all be scientists by the time they're ten,
   And thank the Lord I won't have any children then.

4. The cities will be so overpopulated,
   We'll all be buried from the same apartment house where we were created,
   And if you take a trip to the country somewhere,
   You'll have to be inoculated against fresh air.

5. There'll come a time we'll lose our walking feet,
   And food will all be predigested so we won't have to eat,
   And children will be made in test-tubes, so we won't have to wed,
   And thank God by that time I will be dead.

   Chorus: *(last time)*

   There'll come a time,
   Won't you be proud,
   And by that time I'll be playing an unamplified harp
   On an eighteenth century cloud.

whose garden was this?

Words and music by Tom Paxton

Chorus:

Whose garden was this?
It must have been lovely.
Did it have flowers?
I've seen pictures of flowers,
And I'd love to have smelled one!

1. Whose river was this?
   You say it ran freely?
   Blue was its color?
   I've seen blue in some pictures,
   And I'd love to have been there!
   Ah, tell me again, I need to know:
   The forest had trees,
   The meadows were green,
   The oceans were blue,
   And birds really flew,
   Can you swear that was true?

2. Whose gray sky was this?
   Or was it a blue one?
   Nights there were breezes?
   I've heard records of breezes,
   And you tell me you felt one.
   Ah, tell me again, I need to know:
   The forest had trees,
   The meadows were green,
   The oceans were blue,
   And birds really flew,
   Can you swear that was true?

the cement octopus

Words and music by Malvina Reynolds

1. There's a cement octopus sits in Sacramento, I think,
   Gets red tape to eat, gasoline taxes to drink,
   And it grows by day and it grows by night,
   And it rolls over everything in sight,
   Oh, stand by me and protect that tree
   From the freeway misery.

2. Who knows how the monster started to grow that way,
   Its parents are frightened and wish it would go away,
   But the taxes keep coming, they have to be spent
   On big bulldozers and tanks of cement,
   Oh, stand by me and protect that tree
   From the freeway misery.

3. That octopus grows like a science-fiction blight,
   The Bay and the Ferry Building are out of sight,
   The trees that stood for a thousand years,
   We watch them falling through our tears,
   Oh, stand by me and protect that tree
   From the freeway misery.

4. Dear old MacLaren won't take this lying down,
   We can hear his spirit move in the sandy ground,
   He built this Eden on the duney plain,
   Now they're making it a concrete desert again,
   Oh, stand by me and protect that tree
   From the freeway misery.

5. The men on the highways need those jobs, we know,
   Let's put them to work planting new trees to grow,
   Building new parks where kids can play,
   Pushing that cement monster away,
   Oh, stand by me and protect that tree
   From the freeway misery.

simpson creek
won't never run clean again

By Mayf Nutter

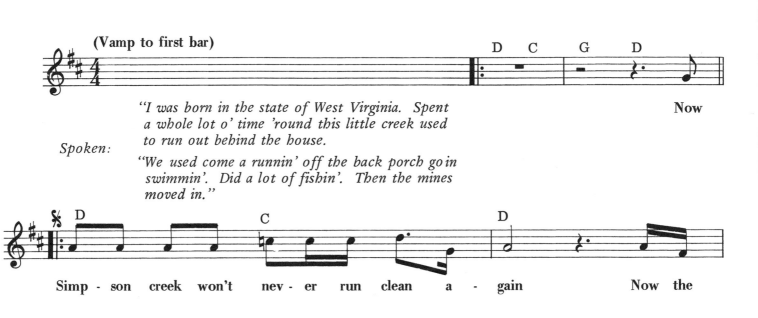

(Vamp to first bar)

D C G D

Now

Spoken:

"I was born in the state of West Virginia. Spent a whole lot o' time 'round this little creek used to run out behind the house.

"We used come a runnin' off the back porch goin swimmin'. Did a lot of fishin'. Then the mines moved in."

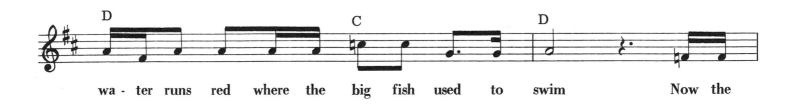

D   C   D

Simp - son creek won't nev - er run clean a - gain   Now the

D   C   D

wa - ter runs red where the big fish used to swim   Now the

G   F   D

fish all died__ and there ain't no sum-mer time   swim-min' hole   Since the

F   C   D

men moved in   o - pened up the hills start - ed load - in' gold __

Oh! Lord what have we done___ wi' the land you trust-ed us___ to run___ The

land that fed and clothed us well___ we made an Ap - pa - la - chian hill___
Chorus, Verse 2: we made in - to a hun - gry hell.

Now the

Oh Lord what have we done___ with the land you trust-ed us___ to run,___ The

land that fed and clothed us well___ we've made an Ap - pa - la chian hill _____ The

Simp - son creek won't nev - er run clean a - gain.

1. Now Simpson Creek
   Won't never run clean again.
   Now the water runs red
   Where the big fish used to swim.
   Now the fish all died
   And there ain't no summer time swimmin' hole
   Since the men moved in
   Opened up the hills started loadin' gold.

2. Now West Fork River
   Won't never run clean again
   Least not from the spot
   Where Simpson Creek dumps in.
   Yeah, the mines closed up
   But the hillsides keep on slidin' down
   Where the strip mines cut
   And there ain't no trees where they used to hang down.

Chorus:

Oh! Lord what have we done
Wi' the land you trusted us to run.
The land that fed and clothed us well
We made an Appalachian hill.

once there was

Words and music by Dottie Gittelson

82

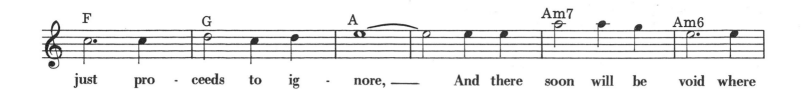

just pro - ceeds to ig - nore, —— And there soon will be void where

man has de - stroyed, for the wells keep on dril - ling and the oil keeps on

spil - ling and the air keeps on fil - ling and —— man keeps on

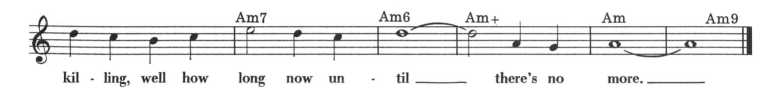

kil - ling, well how long now un - til —— there's no more. ————

1. Once there was land as nature had planned,
   White sparkling sand on the shore,
   But with the passage of time, it's covered with slime,
   And the land that we knew is no more,
   The land that we knew is no more.

2. Once there were waters, translucent and bright,
   Teeming with life by the score,
   But we've polluted the lake and the ocean's opaque,
   And the waters we knew are no more,
   The waters we knew are no more.

3. Once there was air, fresh, free and fair,
   To breathe when we opened the door,
   But now how we choke from the smog and the smoke,
   And the air that we knew is no more,
   The air that we knew is no more.

4. Once there were creatures abounding with life,
   And they flourished in freedom before,
   But where once they had thrived, only few have survived,
   And the wildlife we knew is no more, no more.

5. Yes, once there were seas, and once there were trees,
   In a world to enjoy and explore,
   And once there was man, who takes what he can,
   And just proceeds to ignore,
   And there soon will be void where man has destroyed,
   For the wells keep on drilling and the oil keeps on spilling,
   And the air keeps on filling and man keeps on killing,
   Well, how long now until – there's no more?

amazon song

By Mark Spoelstra

chase the sun my riv-er run whis-tle in the wind — Do — you re-
mem - ber Do — you re - mem - ber
Do — you re - mem-ber Do — you re - mem-ber Do — you re - mem-ber

Riff on out

1. Foot loose and fancy free, nothin' can worry me
   Gonna go back, yes, I remember when we were kids, how we could live
   Rollin' on a river free of time
   Summertime huckleberry
   Summertime huckleberry, take me back to the rollin' river.

2. I'm gonna float down the Amazon on my rubber raft
   Rollin' down the river boys, I ain't comin' back
   Gonna chase the sun, my river run, whistle in the wind — do you remember,
   Do you remember.

3. Snapdragons and bumblebees, lemonade and climbin' trees
   Gonna go back, yes, I remember, now we could build a fort then tear it down
   Ourselves, of course, rollin' on a river free of time
   Treehouse with a tire swinging, dusty toes, mama singing
   Take me back to the rollin' river.

4. I'm gonna float down the Amazon on my rubber raft
   Rollin' down the river boys, I ain't comin' back
   Gonna chase the sun, my river run, whistle in the wind — do you remember,
   Do you remember.

goodbye to the 30ft trailer

By Ewan MacColl

Moderately

The auld ways are chang - ing, ye can - na de - ny, The day o' the trav - el -ler's o - ver, There's no - where to gang and there's no - where to bide, So fare - weel to the life o' the rov - er.

Chorus:

Good - bye to the tent and the old car - a - van To the tin - ker, the gyp - sy, the trav - el - ling man, And good - bye to the thir - ty - foot trail - er.

1. The auld ways are changing, ye canna deny,
   The day o' the traveller's over,
   There's nowhere to gang and there's nowhere to bide,
   So fareweel to the life o' the rover.

   Chorus:
   Good-bye to the tent and the old caravan
   To the tinker, the gypsy, the travelling man,
   And goodbye to the thirty-foot trailer.

2. Fareweel to the cant and the travelling tongue,
   Fareweel to the Romany talking,
   The buying and selling, the old fortune-telling,
   The knock on the door and the hawking.

3. You've got to move fast to keep up wi' the times,
   For these days a man canna daunder;
   There's a byelaw to say you maun be on your way
   And another to say you can't wander.

4. The auld ways are passing and soon they'll be gone,
   For progress is aye a big factor;
   It's sent tae afflict us and when they evict us
   They tow us away wi' a tractor.

5. Fareweel to the pony, the cob and the mare,
   The reins and the harness are idle;
   You don't need the strap when you're breaking up scrap
   So fareweel to the bit and the bridle.

6. Fareweel to the fields where we've sweated and toiled,
   At pu'in', and shawin' and liftin',
   They'll soon hae machines and the travelling quaens,
   And their menfolk had better be shifting.

my dirty stream

By Peter Seeger

Moderately

Sail - ing down my dir - ty stream ___ Still I love it and I'll keep the

dream ___ That some day though may - be not this year ___

___ My Hud - son Riv - er will once a - gain run clear. ___ It starts

high in the moun - tains of the North ___ Crys - tal clear and

i - cy trick - les forth ___ With just a few float - ing wrap-pers of chew - ing

gum ___ Dropped by some hik - ers to warn of things to come. ___

1. Sailing down my dirty stream
   Still I love it and I'll keep the dream
   That some day though maybe not this year
   My Hudson River will once again run clear.
   It starts high in the mountains of the North
   Crystal clear and icy trickles forth
   With just a few floating wrappers of chewing gum
   Dropped by some hikers to warn of things to come.

2. At Glens Falls, five thousand honest hands
   Work at the Consolidated Paper Plant
   Five million gallons of waste a day
   Why should we do it any other way?
   Down the valley one million toilet chains
   Find my Hudson so convenient place to drain
   And each little city says, "Who, me?
   Do you think that sewage plants come free?"

3. In the great ocean they say the water's clear
   But I live at Beacon pier here
   Half way between the mountains and sea
   Tacking back and forth, this thought returns to me
   Sailing up my dirty stream
   Still I love it and I'll dream
   That some day though maybe not this year
   Yes, my Hudson and my country will run clear.

DDT on my brain

Words and music by Malvina Reynolds

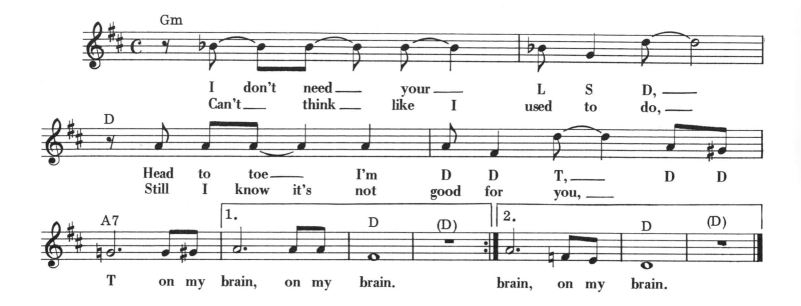

1. I don't need your L S D,
   Head to toe I'm D D T,
   D D T on my brain,
   On my brain.
   Can't think like I used to do,
   Still I know it's not good for you,
   D D T on my brain,
   On my brain.

2. They spray the wheat the chickens eat,
   It's in my eggs, it's in my meat
   D D T on my brain,
   On my brain.
   It kills the bugs in the apple tree,
   I eat the pie and it's killing me.
   D D T on my brain,
   On my brain.

3. All the farms they get that spray,
   It washes down into my Bay
   D D T on my brain,
   On my brain.

It kills the crabs, it kills the fish,
It shines up from my supper dish.
D D T on my brain,
On my brain.

4. Falcon's flying wild and free,
   His babies die of the D D T
   D D T on my brain,
   On my brain.
   Chemical stocks are riding high,
   Farm field workers spray and die.
   D D T on my brain,
   On my brain.

5. Bring back the bugs in my apple tree,
   Don't lay that poison spray on me
   D D T on my brain,
   On my brain.
   I don't need your L S D,
   D D T is killing me.
   D D T on my brain,
   On my brain.

the plodder seam

By Ewan MacColl

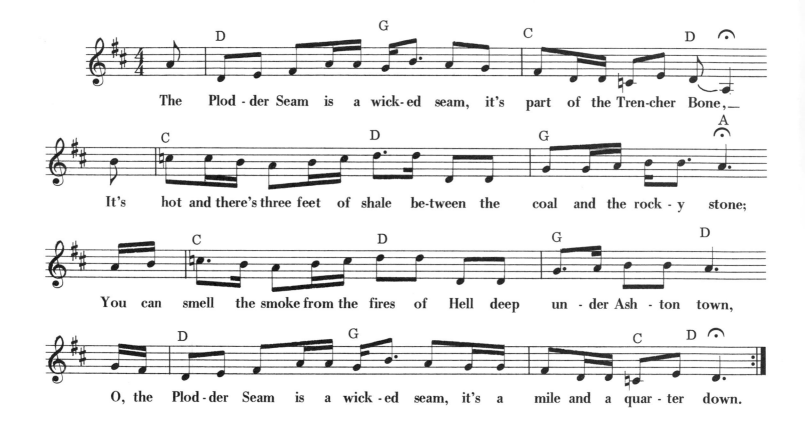

The Plod-der Seam is a wick-ed seam, it's part of the Tren-cher Bone,__
It's hot and there's three feet of shale be-tween the coal and the rock-y stone;
You can smell the smoke from the fires of Hell deep un-der Ash-ton town,
O, the Plod-der Seam is a wick-ed seam, it's a mile and a quar-ter down.

1. The Plodder Seam is a wicked seam,
   It's part of the Trencher Bone,
   It's hot and there's three feet of shale
   Between the coal and the rocky stone;
   You can smell the smoke from the fires of Hell
   Deep under Ashton town,
   O, the Plodder Seam is a wicked seam,
   It's a mile and a quarter down.

2. Thirteen-hundred tons a day
   Are taken from that mine,
   There's a ton of dirt to a ton of rock
   And a gallon of sweat and grime.
   You crawl behind the cutters
   And you scrabble for the coal;
   I'd rather sweep the streets
   Than have to burrow like a mole.

black waters

By Jean Ritchie

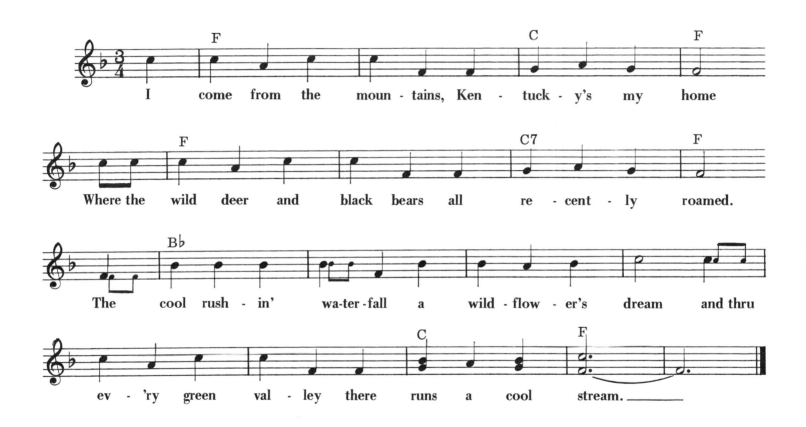

I come from the moun-tains, Ken-tuck-y's my home

Where the wild deer and black bears all re-cent-ly roamed.

The cool rush-in' wa-ter-fall a wild-flow-er's dream and thru

ev-'ry green val-ley there runs a cool stream._____

1. I come from the mountains, Kentucky's my home
   Where the wild deer and black bears all recently roamed
   The cool rushin' waterfall a wild flower's dream
   And thru every green valley there runs a clear stream.

   Now's there's scenes of destruction on every hand
   Black Waters, Black Waters, run down thru my land.

2. Oh the quail's a pretty bird, she sings a sweet song
   And the woods of tall timbers where she nests her young
   And the voices of the small birds will sound their names
   And the hillsides come a-slidin' so awful and grand
   And the floodin' Black Waters come over my land.

3. In the horizon of springtime we planted our corn
   In the end of the springtime we buried our son

   In the summer a nice man says everything's fine
   An employer just requires a way to his mine
   And they threwdown the mountain and covered the corn
   And the hillside is now a mile deeper down
   And there he sat with his hat in his hand
   And he poisoned our waters that run o'er our land.

4. Well I ain't got much money and much of a home
   I own my own land but my land's not my own
   But if I had 10 million somewhere thereabouts
   I'd buy Kerry county and run 'em all out
   And sit down on my bank with a plate and can
   And watch the clear waters run over my land
   And it would be like the ol' promised land
   Black waters, black waters no more in my land.

we can't get there from here

Words and music by John Edmiston

1. Yesterday and leaves against the sun
   Falling leaves today one by one
   And the things that once ran wild and free
   Fast becoming things that used to be.

   Chorus:
   Let the rivers flow and the seeds will grow
   And a fresh wind will come blowing year by year
   'Cause we can't get there from here, not from here.

2. Hear the echoes come from far and near
   Grains of life are sifting, tear by tear
   Crying from the mountains to the seas
   Ev'rywhere they're dying, can't you see?

3. Now the air is dark that once was clear
   And the rose is gone that once grew here
   Here and there a dead bird on the ground
   And an oilslick looms for miles around.

4. There's a long grey haze across this land
   Troubled waters flowing to the sand
   And it's going to spread from shore to shore
   Till there's nothing left here anymore.

castles in the air

Written by Don McLean

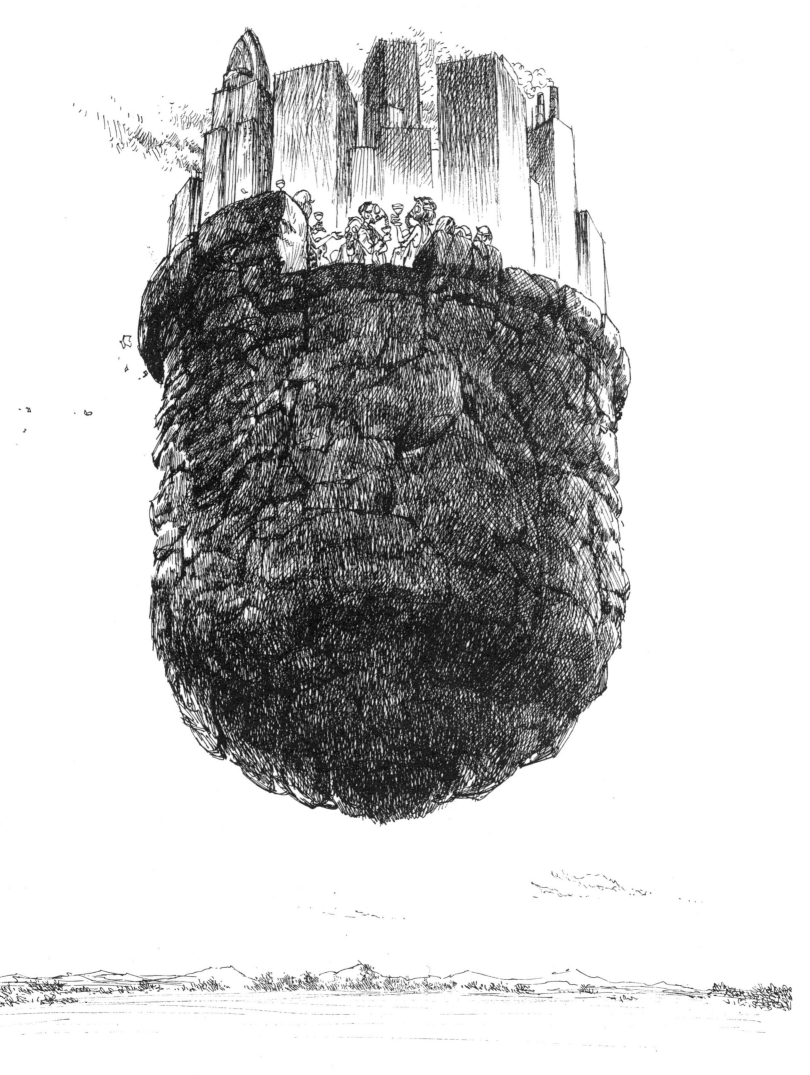

say my last good - bye _____ The love we knew _____ ain't

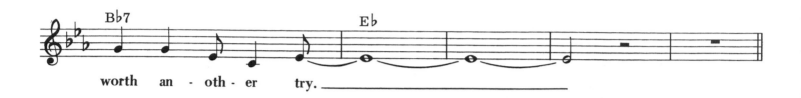

worth an - oth - er try. _____

Chorus:

Save me from all the trou - ble and the pain, ___ I know I'm

weak but I can't face that girl a - gain _____

_____ Tell her the rea - sons

why I can't re - main ___ Per - haps she'll un - der -

stand if you tell it to her plain. _____

1. And if she asks you why
   You can tell her that I told you
   That I'm tired of castles in the air
   I've got a dream I want the world to share
   And castle walls just lead me to despair.

   Hills of forest green where the mountains touch the sky
   A dream come true I'll live there till I die.
   I'm asking you to say my last goodbye
   The love we knew ain't worth another try.

   Chorus:

   Save me from all the trouble and the pain,
   I know I'm weak but I can't face that girl again.
   Tell her the reasons why I can't remain
   Perhaps she'll understand if you tell it to her plain.

2. But how can words express the feel
   Of sunlight in the morning
   In the hills away from city strife
   I need a country woman for my wife
   I'm city born but I love the country life.

   For I will not be part of the cocktail generation
   Partners waltz devoid of all romance.
   The music plays and everyone must dance.
   I'm bowing out, I need a second chance.

love our river again

Words and music by Jimmy Collier and Peter Hennessy

Chorus:

We've got to learn ___ to love our riv-er a - gain ___

We've got to learn to treat our riv - er like a friend ___

For if we don't, it will soon be the end! ___

We've got to learn ___ to love our riv - er a - gain. ___

Verse:

* { There's a Hud -son Riv - er sloop, sail - ing on the riv - er to - day.
A This is the first time in a cen - tu -ry or so .
sym -bol of the time when the wa - ter was pure and clean.
That's the way it was a cen - tu -ry a - go. }

*Vary the melody of the verse line to fit the words, as needed.

Chorus:

We've got to learn to love our river again
We've got to learn to treat our river like a friend
For if we don't, it will soon be the end!
We've got to learn to love our river again.

1. There's a Hudson River sloop, sailing on the river today
   This is the first time in a century or so
   A symbol of the time when the water was pure and clean
   That's the way it was a century ago.

2. There's a Hudson River sloop, sailing on the river this week
   To welcome her, let's turn the whole town out
   I've seen everything in the river from abandoned cars to you-know-what
   And if we work together we can make life better for us all.

3. A long time ago there were game along these banks
   Happy smiling people everywhere
   Then progress came to pass
   And the beauty of the river and the people could not last
   And now people aren't sure which way to go
   And all we are saying is something you should already know.

(last Chorus)

We've got to learn to love our neighbor again
We've got to learn to treat our neighbor like a friend
For if we don't, it will soon be the end!
We've got to learn to love our neighbor again.

preserven el parque elysian

By Mike Kellin

Que lin - do el par - que E - ly - sian! _____ Que

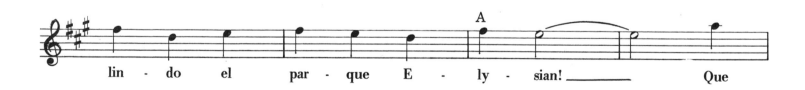

lin - do el par - que E - ly - sian! _____ Que

lin - do! (Que lin - do!) Que lin - do! (Que lin - do!) Que

lin - do el par - que E - ly - sian! _____

1. Que lindo el parque Elysian!
   Que lindo el parque Elysian!
   Que lindo! (que lindo!)
   Que lindo! (que lindo!)
   Que lindo el parque Elysian!
      (Elysian park is beautiful!)

2. Me gusta el parque Elysian!
   (Elysian park is my kind of park!)

3. El aire es libre, amigos!
   (The air is free, my friends!)

4. No queremos fincas en el parque!
   (We don't want building in the park!)

5. Queremos el zacate verde!
   (We want the green grass!)

6. El parque es suyo y mio!
   (The park is yours and mine!)

7. Los niños necesitan el parque!
   (The children need the park!)

8. Preservan el parque Elysian!
   (Save Elysian park!)

9. No Pasaran Los Bulldozers!
   (Stop The Bulldozers!)

what have they done to the rain?

Words and music by Malvina Reynolds

1. Just a little rain falling all around,
   The grass lifts its head to the heavenly sound,
   Just a little rain, just a little rain,
   What have they done to the rain?

2. Just a little breeze out of the sky,
   The leaves pat their hands as the breeze blows by,
   Just a little breeze with some smoke in its eye,
   What have they done to the rain?

3. Just a little boy standing in the rain,
   The gentle rain that falls for years.
   And the grass is gone, the boy disappears,
   And rain keeps falling like helpless tears,
   And what have they done to the rain?

the people are scratching

Words by Ernie Marrs and Harold Martin. Music by Peter Seeger.

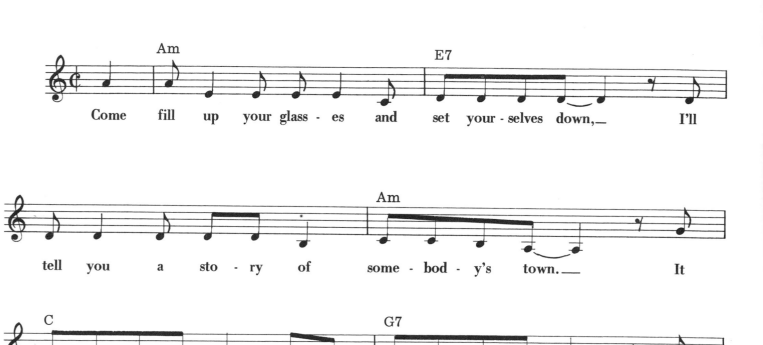

Come fill up your glass - es and set your - selves down,— I'll

tell you a sto - ry of some - bod - y's town.— It

is - n't too near and it's not far a - way—— And ——

— it's not a place where I'd want to stay.

Chorus:

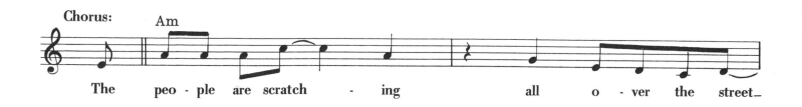

The peo - ple are scratch - ing all o - ver the street—

— Be - cause the rab - bits had noth - ing to eat.

1. Come fill up your glasses and set yourselves down,
   I'll tell you a story of somebody's town.
   It isn't too near and it's not far away
   And it's not a place where I'd want to stay.

   Chorus:
   The people are scratching all over the street
   Because the rabbits had nothing to eat.

2. The winter came in with a cold icy blast,
   It killed off the flowers, and killed off the grass.
   The rabbits were starving because of the freeze
   And they started eating the bark on the trees.

3. The farmers said, "This sort of thing just won't do,
   Our trees will be dead when the rabbits get through;
   We'll have to poison the rabbits, it's clear,
   Or we'll have no crops to harvest next year."

4. So they bought the poison and spread it around
   And soon dead rabbits began to be found.
   Dogs ate the rabbits, and the farmers just said,
   "We'll poison those rabbits 'til the last dog is dead."

5. Up in the sky there were meat-eating fowls
   The rabbits poisoned the hawks and the owls,
   Thousands of field mice the hawks used to chase
   Were multiplying all over the place.

6. The fields and the meadows were barren and brown,
   The mice got hungry and moved into town.
   They city folks took the farmers' advice
   And all of them started to poison the mice.

7. There were dead mice in all the apartments and flats,
   The cats ate the mice, and the mice killed the cats.
   The smell was awful, and I'm glad to say
   I wasn't the man hired to haul them away.

8. All through the country and all through the town
   There wasn't a dog or a cat to be found;
   The fleas asked each other, "Now where can we stay?"
   They've been on the people from then till this day.

9. All you small creatures that live in this land,
   Stay clear of the man with the poisonous hand!
   A few bales of hay might keep you alive,
   But he'll pay more to kill you than to let you survive.

give me back my cool clear water

Words and music by Rick Shaw and Dick Clark

1. Smoke stacks belching clouds of thick black smoke into the sky,
   Cities pumping filth into the rivers running by,
   Highways lined with litter, rusty beer cans ev'rywhere,
   Tell me brother, don't you even care?

   Chorus:

   Give me back my cool, clear, water,
   Give me back my clear, blue, sky,
   Give me back my sparklin' seashore,
   Fish that swim and birds that fly.

2. Off-shore oil wells blacken miles of beaches with their slime,
   And D.D.T. is knocking nature's reason out of rhyme,
   How long can we stand silent and pretend we just don't see?
   When Mother Nature cries to you and me.

3. There are generals who would dump their poison gases in the sea,
   And men who tamper blindly with the world ecology,
   The raven flies across the sun his cryin' fills the day,
   Listen people, hear me when I say,

4. What will be our children's legacy, will they wake to summer's dream?
   Will they know the joy of walking by a crystal mountain stream?
   Will they sail upon the winds and waters flowin' fresh and fair?
   Or will they be the victim of a world that did not care?

the stream goes meandering

Words and music by Mike Kellin

They called in all the en - gin - eers, to make the stream be-have I guess, to

set its course by might and force and slaugh - ter wa - ter cress, but the

Chorus: Andante

stream went me - an - der - ing, me - an - der -

ing, me - an - der - ing, the stream it went me -

an - der - ing, the way that it would go, _____ it

did - n't seem to know _____ it was - n't s'posed to

go the way it seemed to want to go _____ (From)

1. They called in all the engineers, to make the stream behave I guess,
   To set its course by might and force and slaughter water cress,

   Chorus:
   But the stream went meandering, meandering, meandering,
   The stream it went meandering, the way that it would go,
   It didn't seem to know it wasn't s'posed to go
   The way it seemed to want to go.

2. From M.I.T. and Rensselaer they came a-singing "Have no fear,
   We'll see it through 'cause we can do," and they set up a mighty cheer!

3. They gave the stream a concrete bed, with conduits of steel and lead
   And the engineers who had no peers declared that the stream was dead.

4. The engineers were in a pickle, they built a dam of plated nickel
   They wouldn't be downed, for they were bound to harness the mighty trickle.

5. The Senate nearly blew its top, they said we'll clear this up chop chop
   They met on the hill and they passed a bill that ordered the stream to stop.

6. The engineers are at it yet, they've run up quite a fancy debt,
   They're old 'n grey but they won't go 'way as long as the water's wet.

   (Last chorus in present tense — And the stream goes, etc.)

the day the freeway froze

Words and music by Malvina Reynolds

'Twas at eight - o - five A. M. On a hot old Ju - ly
Well the cars be - gan to stop, But the ramps kept feed - ing

day, When a hik - er got on the Gar - field ramp Where he
slow, And a Ply - mouth hard - top Bel - ve - dere was

was - n't sup - posed to be, He was hit by a Fair - lane Riv -
smacked by a Dyn - a - flow. And some of them could have

ier - a With aut - o - mat - ic drive, And a Chev - ro - let Bel
made it, Go - ing out on a ramp marked "in", But no - bod - y does the

Aire cou - pé, And he did - n't stay long a - live. On the
like of that, Be - cause that is a car - di - nal sin.

day the free - way froze in Los An - gel - es, U. S.

A., 'Twas a won - drous af - fair and I

wish I'd been there On the day the free - way froze.

1. 'Twas at eight-o-five A.M.
   On a hot old July day,
   When a hiker got on the Garfield ramp
   Where he wasn't supposed to be,
   He was hit by a Fairlane Riviera
   With automatic drive,
   And a Chevrolet Bel Aire coupé,
   And he didn't stay long alive.

   Chorus:
   On the day the freeway froze in Los Angeles, U.S.A.,
   'Twas a wondrous affair and I wish I'd been there
   On the day the freeway froze.

2. Well the cars began to stop,
   But the ramps kept feeding slow,
   And a Plymouth hardtop Belvedere
   Was smacked by a Dynaflow.
   And some of them could have made it,
   Going out on a ramp marked "in",
   But nobody does the like of that,
   Because that is a cardinal sin.

3. Meantime down in town,
   At the Spring Street underpass,
   A couple of trucks collided,
   And one had a load of gas.
   It could have been a holocaust
   Cause no one could turn about,
   But the engines got up on the cloverleaf
   And they put that fire out.

4. Mr. Gorbach sat at his wheel,
   A hungry man was he,
   And up ahead was an unmanned truck
   From Momma's Bakery.
   He opened the drawer marked "D"
   And found doughnuts glazed and plain,
   And he pulled real hard and the drawer flew out,
   And the doughnuts fell like rain.

5. Well, the people jumped around,
   And the doughnuts soon were gone,
   And Stanley Hackett he had ten,
   But coffee he had none.
   Then somebody found a truck
   That was full of cows and steers,
   And he opened the doors, and the cattle strolled
   Among the lanes and piers.

6. A Bekins Van was stalled,
   And some ladies worked amain,
   And they set themselves up in housekeeping
   In the Harbor "Outbound" lane,
   And a truckload of brassieres
   Was very quickly gone,
   When they all cried "Viva Havana!"
   And tied the arm bands on.

7. The greatest find of all
   Was a wagonload of rum.
   It was all dealt out with a generous hand
   To whoever wanted some,
   And a couple of guys they ran along
   With car tops for their track,
   Wearing "Fight Cancer" sandwich boards
   Which they carried front and back.

8. It was seven hours, they say,
   Till the jam began to go.
   The last lost car was towed away
   After eighty hours or so.
   Three thousand ice cream bars were sold
   To the sound of the auto horn,
   Twenty-three people died that day,
   And three little babes were born.

9. These details can be found
   In City police reports,
   In interviews in the Daily News
   And TV newsreel shorts.
   And all I do is tell to you
   The facts as they arose
   In the city of Los Angeles
   The day the freeway froze.

ma baker's little acre

By John D. Loudermilk

sell her lit - tle a - cre of land _____ She said, "Pa left this

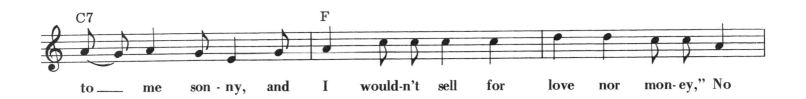

to _____ me son - ny, and I would-n't sell for love nor mon-ey," No

sir, MA BA - KER's gon - na keep her lit - tle a - cre of land _____

_____ Now, the next time they came, they brought the sher - iff, and

found MA a -rock-in' in an old porch chair, just a - knit - tin' and a - rock-in'

out in the eve - ning sun _____ She told them that they'd

best _____ to wait _____ And not to step through the pick - et gate, _____ And

on MA BA - KER's lap they saw Pa's old shot gun _____ Now

out in the mid-dle of the brand_ new lake, is a lit-tle is-land of

one square a-cre, but MA BA-KER's just as hap-py as she can _

be _____ She can't swim, but she_ can float, and

catch big bass from her mo-tor boat, and when the wind ain't blow-in' too

much, she can wa-ter ski _____ and, MA BA-KER still

owns her lit-tle a-cre of land _____ Now, a land _____

Chorus:

Now, a little old lady by the name of MA BAKER
Lived out of town on one square acre,
In a little white house with a picket fence all around.
She had a kind and gentle way
Till the day the T. V. A.
Tried to make MA BAKER sell her little acre of ground.

1. They showed her a map of how the river ran
   And a sketch of the brand new dam,
   But MA BAKER wouldn't sell her little acre of land.
   She said, "Pa left this to me sonny,
   And I wouldn't sell for love nor money,"
   No sir, MA BAKER's gonna keep her little acre of land.

2. Now, the next time they came, they brought the sheriff,
   And found MA a-rockin' in an old porch chair,
   Just a-knittin' and a-rockin' out in the evening sun.
   She told them that they'd best to wait
   And not to step through the picket gate,
   And on MA BAKER's lap they saw Pa's old shot gun.

3. Now out in the middle of the brand new lake,
   Is a little island of one square acre,
   But MA BAKER's just as happy as she can be.
   She can't swim, but she can float,
   And catch big bass from her motor boat,
   And when the wind ain't blowin' too much,
   She can water ski and, MA BAKER still owns her little acre of land.

over the hills

Words by Pete Seeger based on an Irish folk tune

* Sung unaccompanied

Over the hills I went one day
A-dreaming of myself and you.
And the Springtime of years since first we met
And all that we've been through.
May I not with delight still dream of the years
Of the summer and fall to be?
And the many, many verses still to be sung
In the ballad of you and me.

they can't put it back

Words and music by Billy Edd Wheeler

Down in the valley 'bout a mile from me,
Where the crows no longer cry,
There's a great big earth-movin' monster machine,
Stands ten stories high.
The ground he can't eat is a sight,
Takes a hundred tons at a bite.
He can dig up the grass, it's a fact,
But he can't put it back.

They come and tell me I gotta move,
Make way for that big machine,
But I ain't movin', unless they kill me
Like they killed the fish in my stream.
Look at that big machine go.
Took that shady grove a long time to grow.
They can rip it out with one whack,
But they can't put it back.

I never was one to carry signs,
Picket with placards, walk in lines.
Maybe I'm behind the times.
You can bet your sweet life
You're gonna hear it from me.
I ain't gonna take it layin' down.

I'm gettin' tired seein' rocks that bleed their guts on the ground.
I ain't gonna sell my soul,
So they can strip out another little tiny vein of gold.
I ain't movin' out of my track,
'Cause they can't put it back.
They can't put it back.

lamoille river song

By John Nutting

Chorus:

They're clean-ing up our riv-er, ster-i-li-zing our stream. It will be the pur-est that you've ev-er seen. You can run it in your bath-tub, ev-en drink it, too. They're chang-ing the La-moi-lle from dir-ty brown to blue.

Verse:

She wan-ders down thro' Hard-wick, slides a-round the bend; Eats a-way at the print shop and the clean-ers, my friend. Still we love her dear-ly, Ev-en tho' she smells. What-'ll we do ____ with our sew-age? We've al-read-y filled our wells.

Chorus:

They're cleaning up our river,
Sterilizing our stream,
It will be the purest,
That you've ever seen.
You can run it in your bathtub
Even drink it, too
They're changing the Lamoille
From dirty brown to blue.

1. She wanders down through Hardwick
   Slides around the bend
   Eats away at the print shop
   And the cleaners, my friend.
   Still we love her dearly
   Even though she smells.
   What'll we do with our sewage
   We've already filled our wells.

2. They dammed her up in Morrisville
   Made a little lake.
   Old folks set around her
   Their pleasure to take.
   The trout would like her waters
   But the taste, it is too strong,
   One drink of Lake Lamoille
   They'd all be dead and gone.

3. Below the town of Johnson she turns a
      ghastly white.
   Tourists, they have looked at her and
      run away in fright.
   The fishing spots and swimming holes
      get scarcer every day
   She's about become a sewer to float
      our filth away.

4. There's one good thing about her
   She does it every spring,
   Overflows her banks,
   To deposit many things
   Upon the farmer's fields
   And amongst the maple wood.
   All our river needs
   Is to be better understood.

what am i doin' here?

Words and music by Ric Masten

When you're tak-in' that va-ca-tion out in the coun-try-side don't stay too long there in the wil-der-ness 'cause a man seems kind-a small and a moun-tain aw-ful tall it could make you look in-side your-self and ask Where did I come from And uh Uh where am I go-ing And uh what am I do-ing here.

1. When you're takin' that vacation
   Out in the countryside
   Don't stay too long there in the wilderness
   'Cause a man seems kinda small
   And a mountain awful tall
   It could make you look inside yourself and ask...
   Where did I come from
   Where am I goin'
   And what am I doin' here.

2. When you're drivin' in the country
   Keep a-steppin' on the gas
   Hurry, hurry, hurry on your way
   If ya slow down to a walk
   Ya might hear the country talk
   You might hear the country laugh at you and say...
   Where did you come from
   Where are you goin'
   And what are you doin' here.

3. Keep the radio playin'
   And turn the volume up
   Keep your transistor plugged into your ear
   If you listen and you're still
   In the silence of the hills
   Ya might hear things you didn't want to hear...
   Like: where did ya come from
   Where are ya goin'
   And what are you doin' here.

4. Leave your litter in the forest
   And scattered by the road
   So man can feel a little more at home
   The telltale signs of man
   His papers and his cans
   We see 'em and we think we're not alone...
   But where did we come from
   Where are we goin'
   And what are we doin' here.

5. Are we gonna keep a-runnin'
   From the questions that we fear
   Until we bring the whole thing crashin' down
   And on the day we disappear
   There'll be no one left to hear
   The burnin' sky ask the barren ground

      Where did they come from
      And where were they goin'
      And what. . . . .
      Were they doin' here?

to everything there is a season

Words from the Book of Ecclesiastes. Adaptation and music by Pete Seeger.

Refrain:

To ev'rything (turn, turn, turn)
There is a season (turn, turn, turn)
And a time for ev'ry purpose under heaven.

1. A time to be born, a time to die;
   A time to plant, a time to reap;
   A time to kill, a time to heal;
   A time to laugh, a time to weep.

2. A time to build up, a time to break down;
   A time to dance, a time to mourn;
   A time to cast away stones,
   A time to gather stones together.

3. A time of love, a time of hate;
   A time of war, a time of peace;
   A time you may embrace, a time to refrain
   From embracing.

4. A time to gain, a time to lose;
   A time to rend, a time to sew;
   A time to love, a time to hate;
   A time for peace,
   I swear it's not too late.

from way up here

Music by Pete Seeger, words by Malvina Reynolds

(Instrumental, such as whistling, flute, violin or top string of guitar) . . . .

From way up here the earth looks very small,
It's just a little ball of rock and sea and sand,
no bigger than my hand.
From way up here the earth looks very small,
They shouldn't fight at all
down there upon that little sphere.
Their time is short, a life is just a day,
You'd think they'd find a way.
You'd think they'd get along
and fill their sunlit days with song.

From way up here the earth is very small,
It's just a little ball, so small,
so beautiful and clear.
Their time is short, a life is just a day,
Must be a better way
To use the time that runs among the distant suns.

From way up here the earth is very small,
It's just a little ball, so small,
so beautiful and dear.

when you were young

Words and music by Len H. Chandler, Jr.

CAPO SECOND FRET*

* Len has named the chords by their true tones, so "E Chord" with capo is actually "D," etc.

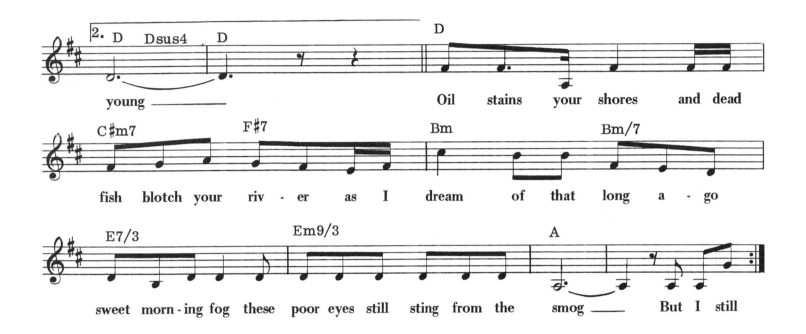

young _____ Oil stains your shores and dead fish blotch your riv - er as I dream of that long a - go sweet morn - ing fog these poor eyes still sting from the smog _____ But I still

1. You're tinting your hair and you wear contact lenses
Your face has been lifted but I can't see the scar
Yes, oh, oh, oh, how well made-up you are.

Chorus:

But I still think of the days
Of your wild wonder ways
And oh what a song could be sung.
You were so beautiful
So beautiful when you were young.

2. Now the oil stains your shores
And dead fish blotch your river
As I dream of that long ago sweet morning fog
These poor eyes still sting from the smog.

we're using up the world

Words and music by Suzanne Harris

Chorus:

We're using up the world,
Can't you see?
Saying that it's all
For you and me.
We're using up the world,
One more time,
And taking away
What's yours and mine.

1. I've seen the mighty redwoods
   Standing a hundred feet high,
   Then along came the loggingmen
   And chopped them all down
   And left a big hole in the sky.

2. Factories by the thousand
   Are turning the rivers black,
   And the working man says:
   'It's hard to make a living
   But easy to turn your back.'

3. Smoke and dust and oil and soot
   Fill every breath we breathe,
   So now it costs us our very life
   To have what once was free. (Cho.)

4. We can always blame the government
   Or men in foreign lands,
   But we're the ones
   Who've covered the green
   With rusty old cars and tin cans.

5. If you drive across my country
   You'll get your just reward,
   For the signs and rhymes
   Unite to tell you
   America's going by the board. (Cho.)

6. There are influential ladies
   Who choose to wear their wealth,
   So the leopard and the tiger
   Are fast disappearing
   As the ladies admire themselves.

7. Some folks go on safari
   Just to watch the animals fall.
   They don't need the meat,
   They've got plenty to eat,
   They just want another trophy for the wall. (Cho.)

8. We can always sing this song again,
   Or tell a story told before,
   But we cannot make earthly things
   Live and breathe once more.

my land is a good land

Words and music by Eric Andersen

My land is a good land   Its grass is made of rain - bow

blades,   Its fields and its riv - ers were blessed by God,   It's a

good land so they say,   It's a good land so they say.

1. My land is a good land,
   Its grass is made of rainbow blades,
   Its fields and its rivers were blessed by God,
   It's a good land, so they say
   It's a good land, so they say.

2. My land is a rich land,
   Its hills and its valleys abound,
   Its highways go to many good places,
   Where many good people are found
   Where many good people are found.

3. My land is a sweet land,
   It's a sweet land, so I've heard,
   Its song is made up of many men's hands,
   And the throat of a humming bird
   And the throat of a humming bird.

4. My land is a free land,
   It's a free land, so I'm told,
   For freedom is a thing that money can't buy,
   And it's worth even more than gold
   And it's worth even more than gold.

5. My land is my homeland,
   And my homeland is a strong land, too,
   It starts where the sun is born each morn,
   And it ends where the skies are blue
   And it ends where the skies are blue.

god bless the grass

Words and music by Malvina Reynolds

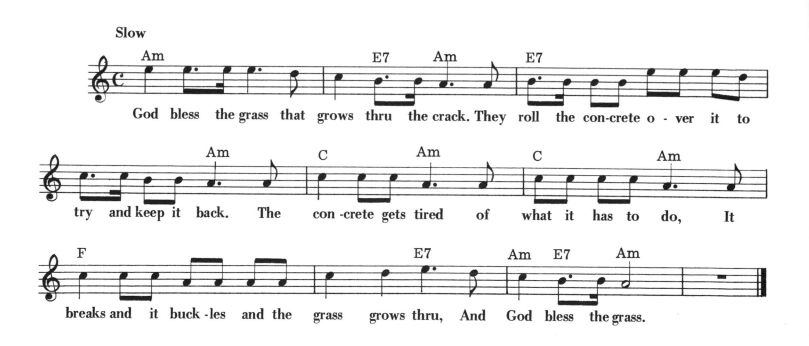

Slow

God bless the grass that grows thru the crack. They roll the con-crete o - ver it to try and keep it back. The con -crete gets tired of what it has to do, It breaks and it buck -les and the grass grows thru, And God bless the grass.

1. God bless the grass that grows thru the crack.
   They roll the concrete over it to try and keep it back.
   The concrete gets tired of what it has to do,
   It breaks and it buckles and the grass grows thro,
   And God bless the grass.

2. God bless the truth that fights toward the sun,
   They roll the lies over it and think that it is done.
   It moves through the ground and reaches for the air,
   And after a while it is growing everywhere,
   And God bless the grass.

3. God bless the grass that breaks through cement.
   It's green and it's tender and it's easily bent,
   But after a while it lifts up its head,
   For the grass it is living and the stone it is dead,
   And God bless the grass.

4. God bless the grass that's gentle and low,
   Its roots they are deep and its will is to grow.
   And God bless the truth, the friend of the poor,
   And the wild grass growing at the poor man's door,
   And God bless the grass.

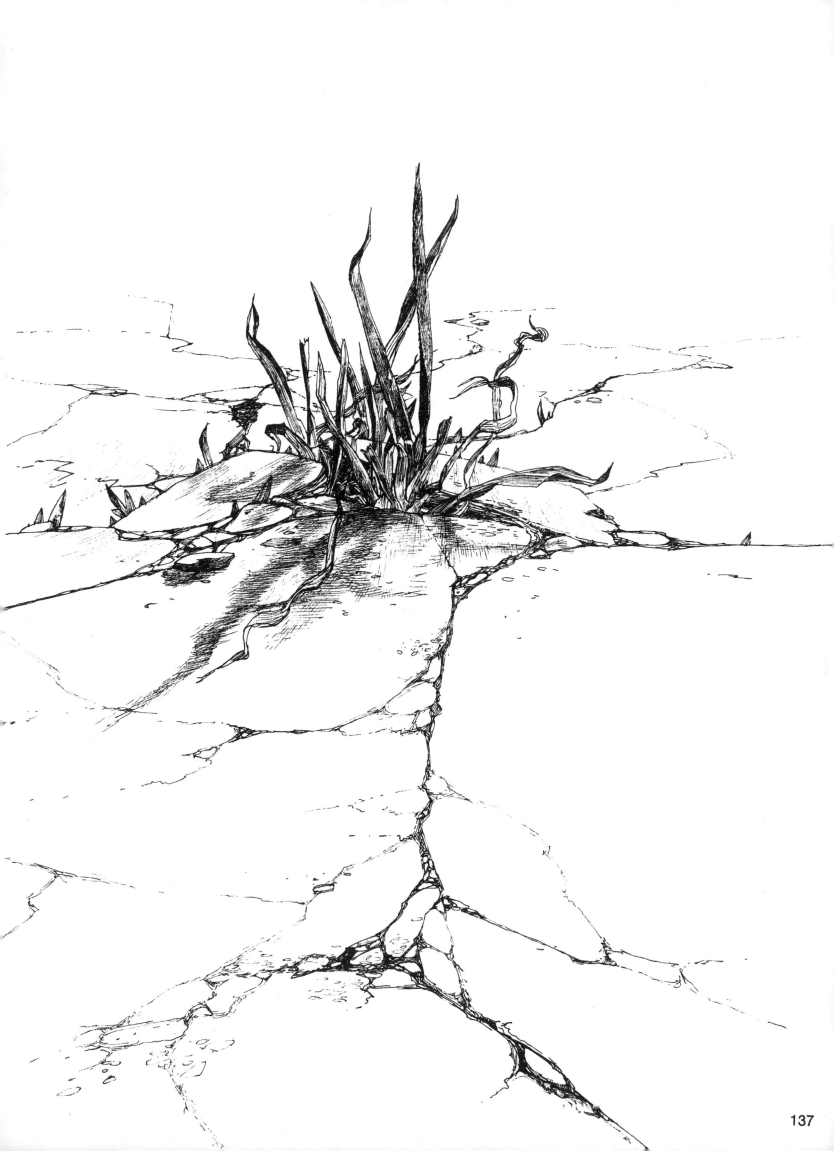

Alphabetical listing

Song title

Song title

Index of first lines

33⅓ LP record guide

Not every song in this anthology has been recorded. Others were recorded some time ago on 45 rpms, which we are not listing. A few were recorded on labels that no longer exist.

With this in mind, we cannot claim that this LP guide is complete. What LP guide is?

Title	Recording artist[1]	Record
Amazon Song	Mark Spoelstra	North Star (to be released)
Black Waters	Jean Ritchie	Sire 97014
Castles in the Air	Don McLean	Mediarts 41-4
Coyote, My Little Brother	Peter LaFarge	Folkways FN 2532
Coyote, My Little Brother	Pete Seeger	Columbia CL 2432
Cement Octopus, The	Pete Seeger	Columbia CL 2432
Children's House	Toni Brown	Capitol (to be released)
Coming of the Roads	Judy Collins	Elektra EKS 7300
Cannonsville Dam	Grant Rogers	Folk-Legacy FSA 27
Day the Freeway Froze, The	Malvina Reynolds	Folkways FN 2524
DDT on My Brain	Malvina Reynolds	Century City CCR 5100
Faucets Are Dripping, The	Malvina Reynolds	Folkways FN 2524
Faucets Are Dripping, The	Pete Seeger	Columbia CL 2432
From Way Up Here	Malvina Reynolds	Century City CCR 5100
From Way Up Here	Pete Seeger	Columbia CL 2432
God Bless the Grass	Malvina Reynolds	Columbia CS 9414
God Bless the Grass	Pete Seeger	Columbia CL 2432
Goodbye to the 30 ft. Trailer	Ian Campbell Folk Group	Elektra 7309
Hand of Man, The	Joe McDonald	Vanguard VSD6555
Here Come the Beautiful People	Suzanne Harris	Special record for *Animals* magazine[2]
Lamoille River Song	Caroline & Sandy Paton	Folk-Legacy EGO-30
Let It Be	Malvina Reynolds	Century City CCR 5100
Let It Be	Malvina Reynolds	Folkways FN 2524
Little Boxes	Malvina Reynolds	Columbia CS 9414
Little Boxes	Pete Seeger	Columbia CS 8901
Little Boxes	Pete Seeger	Columbia 9416
Loneliness	Ric Masten	Special record for Unitarian Universalist Assoc.[3]

Title	Recording artist[1]	Record
My Dirty Stream	Pete Seeger	Columbia CL 2432
My Land Is a Good Land	Eric Andersen	Vanguard 9206
My Land Is a Good Land	Pete Seeger	Columbia CL 2432
Over the Hills	Pete Seeger	Columbia CL 2705
Orphans of Wealth	Don McLean	Mediarts 41-4
People Are Scratching, The	Pete Seeger	Columbia CL 2432
Pill, The	Pete Seeger	Columbia CS 9303
Pollution	Tom Lehrer	Lehrer Records 862
Preserven El Parque Elysian	Pete Seeger	Columbia CL 2432
Preserven El Parque Elysian	Pete Seeger	Columbia CS 9232
Seventy Miles	The Coachmen	Fantasy F-2482
Seventy Miles	Pete Seeger	Columbia CL 2432
Stream Goes Meandering, The	Mike Kellin	Verve Forecast FT/ FTS 3028
Tapestry	Don McLean	Mediarts 41-4
There'll Come a Time	Malvina Reynolds	Century City CCR 5100
To Everything There Is a Season	Pete Seeger	Columbia CS 9416
To Everything There Is a Season	Pete Seeger	Columbia CS 8716
To Everything There Is a Season	Leon Bibb	RCA Victor LSP 4298
To Everything There Is a Season	Judy Collins	Elektra EKS 7243
To Everything There Is a Season	Judy Collins	Elektra EKS 74055
We Can't Get There from Here	Val Stoecklein	Happy Tiger HT 1008
We Will All Go Together When We Go	Tom Lehrer	Reprise 6199
We're Using Up the World	Suzanne Harris	Special record for Animals magazine[2]
What Am I Doin' Here?	Ric Masten	Special record for Unitarian Universalist Assoc.[3]
What Have They Done to the Rain?	Joan Baez	Vanguard 9112
What Have They Done to the Rain?	Malvina Reynolds	Columbia 9414
Whose Garden Was This?	Tom Paxton	Elektra EKS 74066

1 Artist on the recording is not necessarily the writer or composer.
2 Animals magazine, 21 & 22 Great Castle St., London W1N, England.
3 Unitarian Universalist Association, 25 Beacon St., Boston, Mass. 02108.